Weather and Climate Monitoring Protocol

*Eastern Rivers and Mountains Network
and Mid-Atlantic Network*

Natural Resource Report NPS/ERMN-MIDN/NRR—2012/498

Matt Marshall[1], Paul Knight[2], and Jim Comiskey[3]

[1]National Park Service
Eastern Rivers and Mountains Network
420 Forest Resources Building
University Park, Pennsylvania 16802

[2]Pennsylvania State Climate Office
503 Walker Building
Pennsylvania State University
University Park, Pennsylvania 16802

[3]National Park Service
Mid-Atlantic Network
120 Chatham Lane
Fredericksburg, Virginia 22405

March 2012

U.S. Department of the Interior
National Park Service
Natural Resource Stewardship and Science
Fort Collins, Colorado

The National Park Service, Natural Resource Stewardship and Science office in Fort Collins, Colorado publishes a range of reports that address natural resource topics of interest and applicability to a broad audience in the National Park Service and others in natural resource management, including scientists, conservation and environmental constituencies, and the public.

The Natural Resource Report Series is used to disseminate high-priority, current natural resource management information with managerial application. The series targets a general, diverse audience, and may contain NPS policy considerations or address sensitive issues of management applicability.

All manuscripts in the series receive the appropriate level of peer review to ensure that the information is scientifically credible, technically accurate, appropriately written for the intended audience, and designed and published in a professional manner.

This report received formal peer review by subject-matter experts who were not directly involved in the collection, analysis, or reporting of the data, and whose background and expertise put them on par technically and scientifically with the authors of the information.

Views, statements, findings, conclusions, recommendations, and data in this report are those of the author(s) and do not necessarily reflect views and policies of the National Park Service, U.S. Department of the Interior. Mention of trade names or commercial products does not constitute endorsement or recommendation for use by the National Park Service.

This report is available from (http://science.nature.nps.gov/im/units/ermn/ and http://science.nature.nps.gov/im/units/midn/) and the Natural Resource Publications Management website (http://www.nature.nps.gov/publications/NRPM). Please cite this publication as:

NPS 962/113170, March 2012

Revision History

The weather and climate monitoring protocol consists of a narrative (this report) and Standard Operating Procedures (SOPs) that outline specific aspects of the monitoring protocol. The latest versions of the SOPs and additional supporting information can be accessed online at the National Park Service's Eastern Rivers and Mountains Network (http://science.nature.nps.gov/im/units/ermn/) and Mid-Atlantic Network (http://science.nature.nps.gov/im/units/midn/) websites.

The narrative and each SOP have respective revision history logs to document changes in the protocol. The following revision history log is for the narrative.

Version numbers will be incremented by a whole number (e.g., Version 1.3 to 2.0) when a change is made that significantly affects requirements or procedures. Version numbers will be incremented by decimals (e.g., Version 1.3 to Version 1.4) when there are minor modifications that do not affect requirements or procedures included in the protocol. Rows are added to the log as needed for each change or set of changes tied to an updated version number.

Revision History Log

Version #	Date	Revised by	Changes	Justification

Contents

Figures

Tables

Appendixes

List of Key Acronyms

ASOS   Automated Surface Observation System

CASTNet Clean Air Status and Trends Network

COOP   National Weather Service Cooperative Observer Program

CWOP   Citizen Weather Observer Program

ERMN   Eastern Rivers and Mountains Network

FAA   Federal Aviation Administration

GOES   Geostationary Operational Environmental Satellite

IFLOWS   Integrated Flood Observing and Warning System

MIDN   Mid-Atlantic Network

NADP   National Atmospheric Deposition Program

NCDC   National Climatic Data Center

NOAA   National Oceanic and Atmospheric Administration

NPS   National Park Service

NWS   National Weather Service

PASC   Pennsylvania State Climatologist

PDSI   Palmer Drought Severity Index

POR   Period of Record

PRISM   Parameter-elevation Regressions on Independent Slopes Model

RAWS   Remote Automated Weather Stations

RWIS   Road Weather Information System

USDM   United States Drought Monitor

USEPA   United States Environmental Protection Agency

USGS   United States Geological Survey

USHCN   United States Historical Climate Network

Executive Summary

Weather and climate are primary drivers of physical and ecological processes of park resources and therefore critical to park management and visitor experience. For these reasons, weather and climate were identified as a priority vital sign by all National Park Service Inventory and Monitoring Networks including the Eastern Rivers and Mountains and Mid-Atlantic networks.

The goal of this protocol is to utilize existing weather and climate observing networks, stations, and other existing datasets to monitor and record relevant weather elements (e.g., air temperature and precipitation). The intent is to quantify one of the drivers of network park ecosystems, identify trends in these elements, and provide reliable weather and climate data and summaries. Information will be made available to park natural resource managers and other interested parties in concise written reports and from a single, easy to use Internet-based data portal.

The primary monitoring objective is to document current status and long-term trends in air temperature and precipitation at multiple temporal scales (e.g., daily, monthly, seasonal, annual, and decadal) and spatial scales (e.g., individual stations and aggregated stations such as climate divisions) utilizing existing weather and climate monitoring programs and datasets.

This document outlines the rationale and methods proposed for monitoring weather and climate in the Eastern Rivers and Mountains and Mid-Atlantic networks. The protocol narrative explains the rationale for monitoring weather and climate and sets forth the specific monitoring objectives. The narrative also discusses the weather elements to be monitored and provides an overview of the personnel and operational requirements to implement weather and climate monitoring and to report findings. A Standard Operating Procedure (SOP) outlines data management tasks, quality assurance, and delivery of weather and climate data to network staff.

Through data processing, analysis, and reporting, weather and climate data will be made available in a standardized format to support long-term ecological monitoring, other research efforts, park resource management, planning, and interpretation programs.

The weather and climate monitoring protocol consists of a narrative (this report) and Standard Operating Procedures (SOPs) that outline specific aspects of the monitoring protocol. The latest versions of the SOPs and additional supporting information can be accessed online at the National Park Service's Eastern Rivers and Mountains Network (http://science.nature.nps.gov/im/units/ermn/) and Mid-Atlantic Network (http://science.nature.nps.gov/im/units/midn/) websites.

Acknowledgments

The authors would like to recognize and thank several other National Park Service Inventory and Monitoring Networks for the thought and effort that went into the development of their own weather and climate monitoring protocols. We relied heavily on these efforts and want to specifically acknowledge the Greater Yellowstone and Rocky Mountain networks, as well as the Southwest Alaska and North Coast and Cascades networks. We also want to thank several individuals in the Office of the Pennsylvania State Climatologist who each made significant contributions to this project including Tiffany Wisniewski, Chad Bahrmann, Kyle Imhoff, and Sonya Miller. We would also like to thank Brent Frakes, Art DeGaetano, Kelly Redmond, Kathy Penrod, Gregg Kneipp, Stephanie Perles, and Andy Weber for their thorough and valuable reviews.

Introduction

This document outlines the rationale and methods proposed for monitoring weather and climate in the Eastern Rivers and Mountains and Mid-Atlantic networks. The protocol narrative explains the rationale for monitoring weather and climate and sets forth the objectives. The narrative also discusses the specific weather elements to be monitored and provides an overview of the personnel and operational requirements to implement weather and climate monitoring and to report findings. A Standard Operating Procedure (SOP) outlines data management tasks, quality assurance, and delivery of weather and climate data to network staff.

Background and History

Knowing the condition of natural resources in national parks is fundamental to the National Park Service's (NPS) mission to manage park resources "unimpaired for the enjoyment of future generations." Park managers are confronted with increasingly complex and challenging issues that require a broad-based understanding of the status and trends of park resources as a basis for making decisions and working with other agencies and the public for the long-term protection of park ecosystems. The overall purpose of natural resource monitoring in parks is to develop scientifically sound information on the current status and long-term trends in the composition, structure, and function of park ecosystems, and to determine how well current management practices are sustaining those ecosystems (Fancy et al. 2009). Use of monitoring information will increase confidence in manager's decisions and improve their ability to manage park resources, and will allow managers to confront and mitigate threats to the park and operate more effectively in legal and political arenas.

The NPS has initiated a long-term ecological monitoring program, known as "Vital Signs Monitoring," to provide the minimum infrastructure to allow more than 270 national park system units to identify and implement long-term monitoring of their highest-priority measurements of resource condition (Fancy et al. 2009). The term "vital signs" refers to a relatively small set of information-rich attributes that are used to track the overall condition or "health" of park natural resources and to provide early warning of situations that require intervention. Vital signs are defined as a subset of physical, chemical, and biological elements and processes of park ecosystems that are selected to represent the overall health or condition of park resources, known or hypothesized effects of stressors, or elements that have important human values (Fancy et al. 2009). The broad-based, scientifically sound information obtained through this systems-based monitoring program will have multiple applications for management decision-making, research, education, and promoting public understanding of park resources.

NPS Vital Signs Monitoring is implemented programmatically through 32 ecoregional "networks" or groupings of parks linked by geography and shared natural resource characteristics. The network approach, through shared funding and professional staff, also facilitates collaboration, information sharing, and economies of scale.

To be relevant to current management issues and anticipate future issues, monitoring programs must be scientifically credible and produce quality data that is readily accessible and explicitly linked to management decision-making processes. To meet those criteria, explicitly stated goals and objectives are critical. The NPS established (Fancy et al. 2009) programmatic goals for all 32 networks as they plan, design, and implement integrated natural resource monitoring. These goals are to:

1. determine the status and trends of selected indicators of park ecosystem conditions to make better-informed decisions and to work more effectively with other agencies and individuals for the benefit of park resources;
2. provide early warning of abnormal conditions of selected resources to help develop effective mitigation measures and reduce costs of management;
3. provide data to better understand the dynamic nature and condition of park ecosystems and to provide reference points for comparisons with other, altered environments;
4. provide data to meet certain legal and Congressional mandates related to natural resource protection and visitor enjoyment; and
5. provide a means of measuring progress towards performance goals.

The complex task of developing a monitoring program requires a front-end investment in planning and design to ensure that monitoring will meet the critical information needs of each park and produce scientifically credible data that are accessible to managers and other researchers in a timely manner. To that end, each network follows a detailed program development and implementation strategy (Fancy et al. 2009) that includes a peer-reviewed monitoring plan (Marshall and Piekielek 2007, Comiskey and Callahan 2008) and a series of specific, peer-reviewed monitoring protocols that describe how data are to be collected, managed, analyzed, and reported (Oakley et al. 2003).

The Eastern Rivers and Mountains Network (ERMN) includes nine parks in New York, New Jersey, Pennsylvania, and West Virginia (Figure 1). The network includes four smaller parks in central and southwestern Pennsylvania that have a primary cultural or historical focus. These cultural parks are Allegheny Portage Railroad National Historic Site (NHS), Johnstown Flood National Memorial (NMem), Fort Necessity National Battlefield (NB), and Friendship Hill NHS. The remaining five larger parks preserve segments of large rivers and generally extend to the ridge tops surrounding the river section. These river parks are Upper Delaware Scenic and Recreational River (SRR), Delaware Water Gap National Recreation Area (NRA), New River Gorge National River (NR), Gauley River NRA, and Bluestone National Scenic River (NSR).

The Mid-Atlantic Network (MIDN) includes ten parks distributed from southern Pennsylvania to southern Virginia, and extending from the Blue Ridge to the Coastal Plain (Figure 2). The parks are predominantly small, cultural units with a limited history of natural resource monitoring, but the network also includes the comparatively large Shenandoah National Park (NP) located in the Blue Ridge Mountains of Virginia. Richmond National Battlefield Park (NBP), Fredericksburg and Spotsylvania National Military Park (NMP), Petersburg NB, Appomattox Court House National Historical Park (NHP), and Booker T. Washington NMem are also located in Virginia. Gettysburg NMP, Eisenhower NHS, Hopewell Furnace NHS, and Valley Forge NHP are located in Pennsylvania.

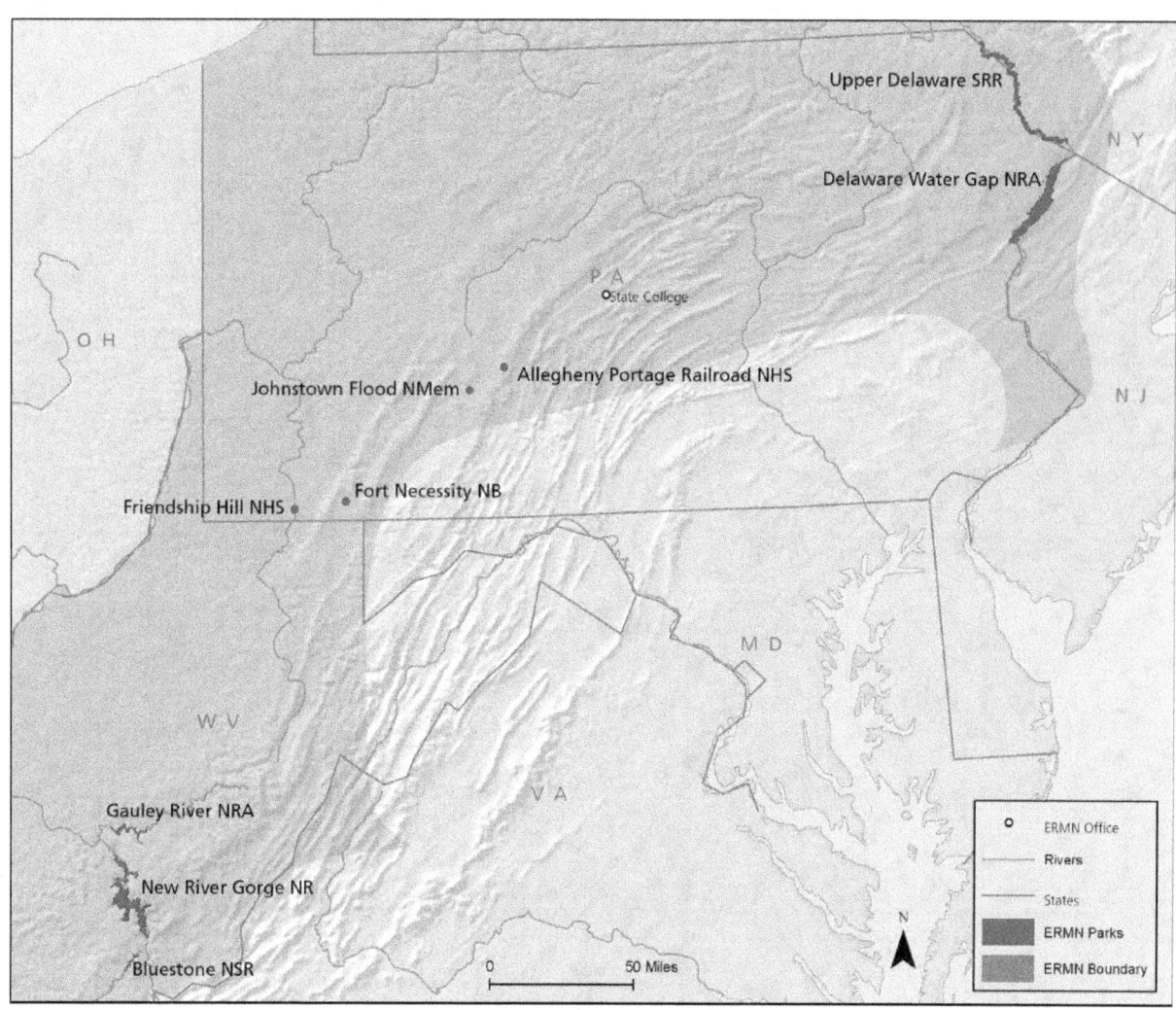

Figure 1. Location of parks in the Eastern Rivers and Mountains Network (ERMN).

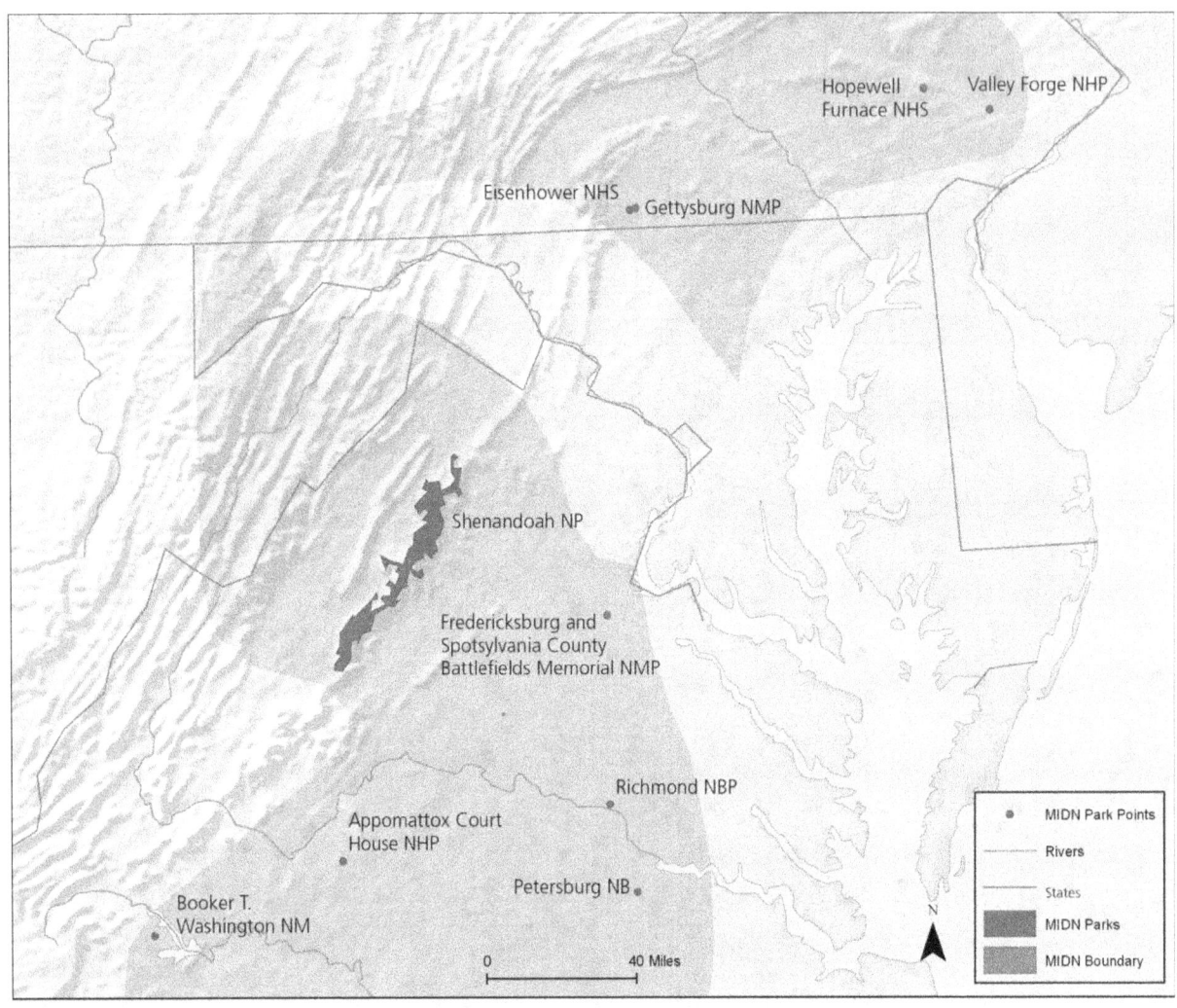

Figure 2. Location of parks in the Mid-Atlantic Network (MIDN).

Rationale for Monitoring Weather and Climate

Monitoring of weather and climate was identified among the highest priority vital signs during the vital signs prioritization process of both networks (Marshall and Piekielek 2007, Comiskey and Callahan 2008). In fact, climate was identified as a priority vital sign by all I&M networks (Fancy et al. 2009) largely because it is a widely recognized driver of terrestrial and aquatic ecosystems, affecting biotic as well as abiotic ecosystem characteristics and processes (Schlesinger 1997, Jacobson et al. 2000, Bonan 2002). Climate is one of the four interactive controls in the conceptual model of ecosystem sustainability (Chapin et al.1996) utilized during both networks' monitoring program development (Marshall and Piekielek 2007, Comiskey and Callahan 2008).

The primary rationale for this protocol is to obtain meteorological information that will be useful in interpreting and understanding changes in species composition and abundance, community structure, water flow and chemistry, and related landscape processes. In short, understanding the role of weather and climate as a driver of park ecosystems is key to understanding other vital signs monitored in the ERMN and MIDN such as vegetation and soils, water quality and benthic macroinvertebrates, and birds. Without weather data, it is difficult to interpret a variety of ecosystem changes—from changes in vegetative cover to shifts in aquatic and terrestrial plant and animal communities.

A secondary rationale for this protocol is to periodically evaluate how weather and climate patterns and trends in the vicinity of these park units compare to regional, national, and even global trends, as well as predicted future changes (e.g., Frumhoff et al. 2007, Karl et al. 2009). These assessments and simply making the data available will be useful to natural resource managers and other NPS personnel and interested parties.

Although the terms weather and climate are sometimes used interchangeably, they differ in temporal perspective. Weather refers to the condition of the atmosphere at a specific point in time or during a short-lived atmospheric event. Climate refers to the aggregation of weather conditions for a location or region and can be defined with averages or representative values for various weather elements. In this document, "weather" generally refers to current (or near-real-time) atmospheric conditions, while "climate" is defined as the complete ensemble of statistical descriptors for temporal and spatial properties of atmospheric behavior for a defined period of record. Climate and weather phenomena shade gradually into each other and are ultimately inseparable (Davey et al. 2006a).

Protocol Focus
This protocol will focus on two primary weather and climate elements (air temperature and precipitation), an integrated element (drought), and several derived elements. A climate (or weather) element is an attribute or property of the state of the atmosphere that is measured or estimated. Examples of climate elements include air temperature, wind speed, wind direction, precipitation, relative humidity, dewpoint, solar radiation, snow depth, soil temperature at a given depth, etc. A derived element is a function of one or more elements (like growing degree days or number of days with rain) and is not measured directly with a sensor.

Air temperature and precipitation are a focus of this protocol because they are key drivers of ecological processes and the most relevant elements to the other vital signs being monitored in the ERMN and MIDN. In addition, multiple high quality measurements are recorded in the immediate vicinity of member parks and historic records are available. Additional weather elements (e.g., wind speed or solar radiation), also with readily available data, may in some cases be of interest and could be addressed (analyzed and reported) periodically but will not be a formal part of the protocol.

Air temperature is a measure of the average kinetic energy in a parcel of air, where the higher the temperature, the faster the molecules are moving. Temperature is measured using thermometers or thermistors shaded from direct sunlight and recorded at varying intervals (e.g., hourly to daily) in degrees Celsius. During the period from 1980 until present, liquid in glass thermometers have been steadily replaced by thermistors, often referred to as MMTS (maximum-minimum temperature sensor), across virtually all networks. The introduction of new sensors has not been without some challenges, as the new instruments have introduced a bias into the temperature records (Lin et al. 2001). However, the most current set of normal temperatures (1981–2010) has a correction factor for this bias (Menne et al. 2009). Air temperature is commonly described and tracked by estimating the average (daily, monthly, seasonal, annual, etc.) minimum and/or maximum and through derived quantities such as the number of days the minimum/maximum deviates from an established threshold or baseline. With knowledge of atmospheric circulation patterns and the influence of topography on temperature, models can be used to interpolate temperatures across space in areas where temperature is not directly recorded. The ERMN and MIDN will monitor temperature because changes in temperatures are a key indicator of climate change, high-quality measurements are recorded from numerous locations in and around the parks, historic temperature records are available, and, most importantly, temperature is a key driver of ecological processes.

Precipitation refers to any product of the condensation of atmospheric water vapor that is deposited on the earth's surface. It can come in many forms, including rain, drizzle, hail, and snow, but does not include dew. Precipitation is measured using a rain gauge and most often recorded as daily total liquid precipitation. Snow, a subset of precipitation and often measured separately, is typically included in rain gauge measures as liquid precipitation after being melted. As with temperature measurements, precipitation is measured at point locations throughout the United States and models and remote sensing such as radar are used to determine the amount and variation in precipitation when and where it is not directly recorded. Unlike temperature, there is a greater degree of local variation in precipitation and precipitation is a discontinuous element (it is not always present like temperature). This presents different challenges for the measurement process. In addition, precipitation has two features of descriptive and impact interest: occurrence (yes/no) and amount (if yes, how much). Temperature does not have these complications. Precipitation is commonly described by total accumulated liquid precipitation (daily, monthly, seasonal, annual, etc.), departures from an established baseline, frequency of precipitation events that exceed an established threshold, number of days with precipitation, and intervals between precipitation events, etc.

Drought is considered an integrative climate element because it is directly dependent on a measured element (in this case, precipitation or snow), tends to be regional in scale, and is often influenced by other climate elements such as air temperature, stream flow, wind, and soil moisture. Drought is difficult to define (see "What is drought?: Understanding and defining drought," National Drought Mitigation Center, 2006, http://drought.unl.edu/whatis/concept.htm). In general, a drought (meteorological, agricultural, or hydrologic) is an extended period of time where an area has a deficiency of precipitation. Drought is a normal, recurrent feature of climate that occurs in virtually all climatic zones, although its effect differs by region. It is important to recognize that drought is a temporary aberration, different from aridity, which is a permanent feature of climate. Because there is no single, precise definition of drought, its onset and termination are difficult to determine and it is measured and described by a variety of metrics. The ERMN and MIDN will monitor and report on drought because it is an important and recurrent phenomenon with ecological consequences.

Derived elements of temperature and precipitation will also be described (e.g., growing degree days, number of days with rain, number of days with snow, number of days the temperature dropped below freezing, etc.). Derived elements are not directly recorded with a sensor, but can be useful for describing weather phenomena. Additional information on the specific derived elements included, and how they are calculated, can be found in the Data Analysis and Reporting section below.

History of Protocol Development and Monitoring Approach

Climatic conditions have been monitored in and around ERMN and MIDN park units largely since the 1940s, with some periods of record extending back to the 1890s through weather and climate monitoring programs administered by other agencies (Table 1). Our monitoring approach is to acquire data from and leverage the expertise of these other programs which provide inexpensive (to the NPS), consistent, long-term, and high-quality records for the region. In Appendix A, we describe the purpose and the data types for each of the extant weather and climate observation networks utilized for this protocol.

Table 1. Weather and climate observation programs/networks with stations in proximity to the Eastern Rivers and Mountains and Mid-Atlantic networks.

Program	Agency
Cooperative Observer Program (COOP)	National Oceanic and Atmospheric Administration (NOAA) -National Weather Service (NWS)
Remote Automated Weather Stations (RAWS)	National Interagency Wildfire Program (U.S. Forest Service, Bureau of Land Management, National Park Service, et al.)
Automated Surface Observation System (ASOS)	National Weather Service / Federal Aviation Administration (FAA) / Department of Defense (DOD)
Clean Air Status and Trends Network (CASTNet)	Environmental Protection Agency (EPA)
National Atmospheric Deposition Program (NADP)	U.S. & State Departments of Agriculture / Multi-agency Collaboration
Integrated Flood Observing and Warning System (IFLOWS)	National Oceanic and Atmospheric Administration
Geostationary Operational Environmental Satellite (GOES)	National Oceanic and Atmospheric Administration
Road Weather Information System (RWIS)	State Departments of Transportation (DOT)
Automated Weather System (AWS)	Proprietary "Weather Bug" Program
Collaborative Community Rain, Hail and Snow Network (CoCoRaHS)	States (e.g., known as the "FROST" program in Pennsylvania)
Citizen's Weather Observer Program (CWOP)	States and National Oceanic and Atmospheric Administration

Early stages of protocol development included inventories of relevant data sources (weather and climate observation networks and stations), surveys of park natural resource managers on weather and climate information needs and currently utilized stations, and prototype weather and climate summary reports. As part of the core inventories of the NPS Inventory and Monitoring Program, the Western Regional Climate Center (WRCC) provided an inventory of point-based monitoring (i.e., weather stations) within and around each NPS unit as well as an overview of the climate of the ERMN and MIDN regions (Davey et al. 2006 a, b). This inventory focused on four federally operated monitoring programs (COOP, RAWS, ASOS, and CASTNet; Table 1). The ERMN and MIDN in collaboration with the Office of the Pennsylvania State Climatologist also produced an inventory of weather stations (Appendix B) which included seven additional regional weather and climate observing networks (Table 1). It should be noted that the CoCoRaHS network (also known as FROST in Pennsylvania), while providing superior precipitation and snow observations, has too short of a period of record for this inventory. This collaboration also included a survey of park natural resource managers (Appendix C) and prototype annual reports (e.g., Knight et al. 2010).

Subsequent sections of this protocol narrative specify the criteria for selecting among the more than 1,250 (>250 ERMN and >1,000 MIDN) available stations identified in these inventories for use in this protocol.

Measurable Objectives

Monitoring objectives were established to meet the overarching vital signs programmatic goals and the rationale for monitoring the resources described above, while clearly articulating what will be measured and the desired outcome of the protocol.

The goal of this protocol is to utilize existing weather and climate observing networks, stations, and other existing datasets to monitor and record relevant primary, integrated, and derived weather elements in order to quantify drivers of network park ecosystems, identify trends in these elements, and provide reliable weather and climate data and summaries to park natural resource managers and other interested parties in concise reports and from a single, easy to use Internet-based portal.

The primary monitoring objective is to:

- document current status and long-term trends in air temperature and precipitation at multiple temporal scales (e.g., daily, monthly, seasonal, annual, and decadal) and spatial scales (e.g., individual stations and aggregated stations such as climate divisions) utilizing existing weather and climate monitoring programs and datasets.

Sampling Design

Ideally, to describe weather and climate within each network and member park and have strong inference to the area of interest, probabilistic (random) sampling would have been used to locate sampling sites (i.e., weather stations). However, this protocol relies on extant weather and climate observing networks and programs and these programs typically used best professional judgement to determine the type, number, and placement of stations. Most stations are located where they are accessible and thought to be representative of an area. Moreover, the goals and objectives of the existing weather and climate observing programs differ, and these differences (appropriately) determined the location of the respective stations. For example, ASOS stations support the needs of the aviation community and the locations of RAWS stations, while generally more remote and away from human inhabited areas were motivated by available Federal agency support and local wildfire threat (Appendix A).

Nonetheless, there is a relatively high density of existing weather and climate observing stations around the ERMN and MIDN parks (ensuring some level of spatial representation) and several high quality stations are located within park boundaries. The relatively long observational period of especially the COOP stations (some dating back to the 1890s) provides an important period of record of historical trends and a basis for evaluating climatic extremes and change. While the "climatic footprint" extends beyond the physical limits of a station, measures from even several stations do not capture the inherent variability of a park's landscape, especially for larger parks (e.g., local precipitation events that do not uniformly affect the entire park) and parks with extensive topographic variability (e.g., temperature differences are closely tied to elevation).

It is important to recognize that these stations are appropriately viewed as a suite of representative "index" sites/stations chosen using best professional judgment and not meant to be part of a formal sampling design that allows inference to entire (or specific) areas of the parks.

Stations Included

Stations included in the monitoring protocol were initially selected from the results of the inventory of weather and climate stations within 40 km of each park conducted by Davey et al. (2006a, b) and those within 100 km of each park conducted by the Office of the Pennsylvania State Climatologist (Appendix B). The >1,250 stations identified in these inventories underwent several qualitative and quantitative levels of "screening" to select a subset of stations that best represent each park's environmental and climatic conditions. Best representation was based on several criteria (Table 2; more fully explained in Appendix B), which included proximity to the park, the representativeness of the station to the park elevation profile (since several weather parameters, most notably temperature, are tightly linked to elevation), the type and frequency of data collection/observation, the period of record, and data availability.

These criteria were used to generate a score for each station to be used as an initial screening tool (Appendix B). Briefly, stations receiving a score ≥20, were currently active (collecting data), and with available data (free and available in near real-time) were selected for further consideration. This first screening step reduced the number of candidate sites to 201 (69 ERMN and 132 MIDN). The second screening step, based on review by park natural resource managers and the authors' judgement, was a decision to eliminate many stations that were located "far" (>40 km) from a park even though a station received a score ≥20 (for a variety of reasons), with

Table 2. Initial criteria used to select among available stations.

Criteria	Description of Criterion
Distance from park	The proximity to the park was calculated by finding the distance from the station to the closest border of the park. Stations farther than 100 km from the park were excluded (most stations are within 40 km of the park border).
Period of Record	Measures the period of record for which data is available for a station. A station must also be currently reporting to be considered.
Reporting Frequency	Based upon how often the station collects weather data (sub-hourly, hourly, or daily).
Reporting Elements	Number of weather elements recorded at a station. Temperature and precipitation scored higher than other elements. Thirteen possible elements.
Data Accessibility	Determined by the amount of data available to the National Climatic Data Center (NCDC) and/or the Office of the Pennsylvania State Climatologist
Park Elevation Distribution	Based upon the elevation of a station and the proportion of the total elevation range of a park that station represents.

the rationale being that these stations likely do not represent within-park weather and climate adequately, given the distance. The initial 100-km radius was selected in an attempt to potentially include high quality stations (such as those at airports) that record a large number of elements (e.g., solar radiation, relative humidity, cloud cover, wind speed, etc.) with a high level of quality assurance that are not routinely collected at many other stations. This logic followed that being used in other I&M networks as well (e.g., Gray 2008). An additional decision to focus the protocol primarily on air temperature and precipitation further substantiated the exclusion of many of these more "distant" stations. We also included stations that were located within park boundaries even if they did not rank highly in the initial screening step, given the inherent interest by park staff in including weather data collected on-site.

Moreover, during this second screening step, two sets of stations were distinguished for analysis and reporting: (1) a larger set of stations with histories of varying length for reporting a snapshot of a year's weather conditions; and (2) a subset of these stations which have long histories and high-quality data to allow analysis of temporal variability and trends (see Data Analysis and Reporting section below). This included consideration of COOP stations that have been designated as United States Historical Climate Network (US HCN) sites (Appendix A).

This second screening step further reduced the candidate stations to 60 (32 ERMN and 28 MIDN). Finally, three additional stations were added to the ERMN list of monitoring stations and four additional stations were added to the MIDN list of monitoring stations. One of the ERMN stations was included in the initial inventories, but excluded because the data were not accessible at that time. Five others (2 ERMN and 3 MIDN) were inadvertently "missed" by both inventories and were subsequently included. One additional station (USGS Stream Gage on Valley Creek) was added to the MIDN list as a source of precipitation data. This resulted in a total of 35 stations used for weather and climate monitoring in the ERMN (Table 3 and Figure 3) and a total of 32 stations used for weather and climate monitoring in the MIDN (Table 3 and Figure 4).

See Appendix D for a complete list of stations selected for use in this monitoring protocol. These 67 selected stations constitute the core set of stations that will be utilized for both annual reporting (all stations) and periodic "variability and trends" reporting (28 stations; see below).

Table 3. Total number of stations used for monitoring weather and climate in the ERMN and MIDN listed by park. Numbers in parentheses indicate the number of stations located within park boundaries. See Table 1 for definition of weather and climate observation network acronyms.

Network/Park Unit	Total Stations	COOP	RAWS	ASOS	CASTNet	RWIS	USGS
ERMN	35 (5)	26 (2)	4 (3)	5	0	0	0
Allegheny Portage Railroad NHS	3	3	0	0	0	0	0
Johnstown Flood NMem	2	1	0	1	0	0	0
Fort Necessity NB	3	3	0	0	0	0	0
Friendship Hill NHS	3	2	0	1	0	0	0
Upper Delaware SRR	7 (2)	7 (2)	0	0	0	0	0
Delaware Water Gap NRA	6 (2)	2	2 (2)	2	0	0	0
Gauley River NRA	2	2	0	0	0	0	0
New River Gorge NR	5 (1)	3	1 (1)	1	0	0	0
Bluestone NSR	4	3	1	0	0	0	0
MIDN	32 (4)	17	2 (2)	9	2 (1)	1	1 (1)
Shenandoah NP	9 (3)	5	2 (2)	1	1 (1)	0	0
Hopewell Furnace NHS	3	2	0	1	0	0	0
Valley Forge NHP	3 (1)	1	0	1	0	0	1 (1)
Eisenhower NHS/Gettysburg NMP	2	1	0	0	1	0	0
Fredericksburg and Spotsylvania NMP	6	4	0	2	0	0	0
Richmond NBP	2	0	0	1	0	1	0
Petersburg NB	2	1	0	1	0	0	0
Appomattox Court House NHP	2	1	0	1	0	0	0
Booker T. Washington NM	3	2	0	1	0	0	0

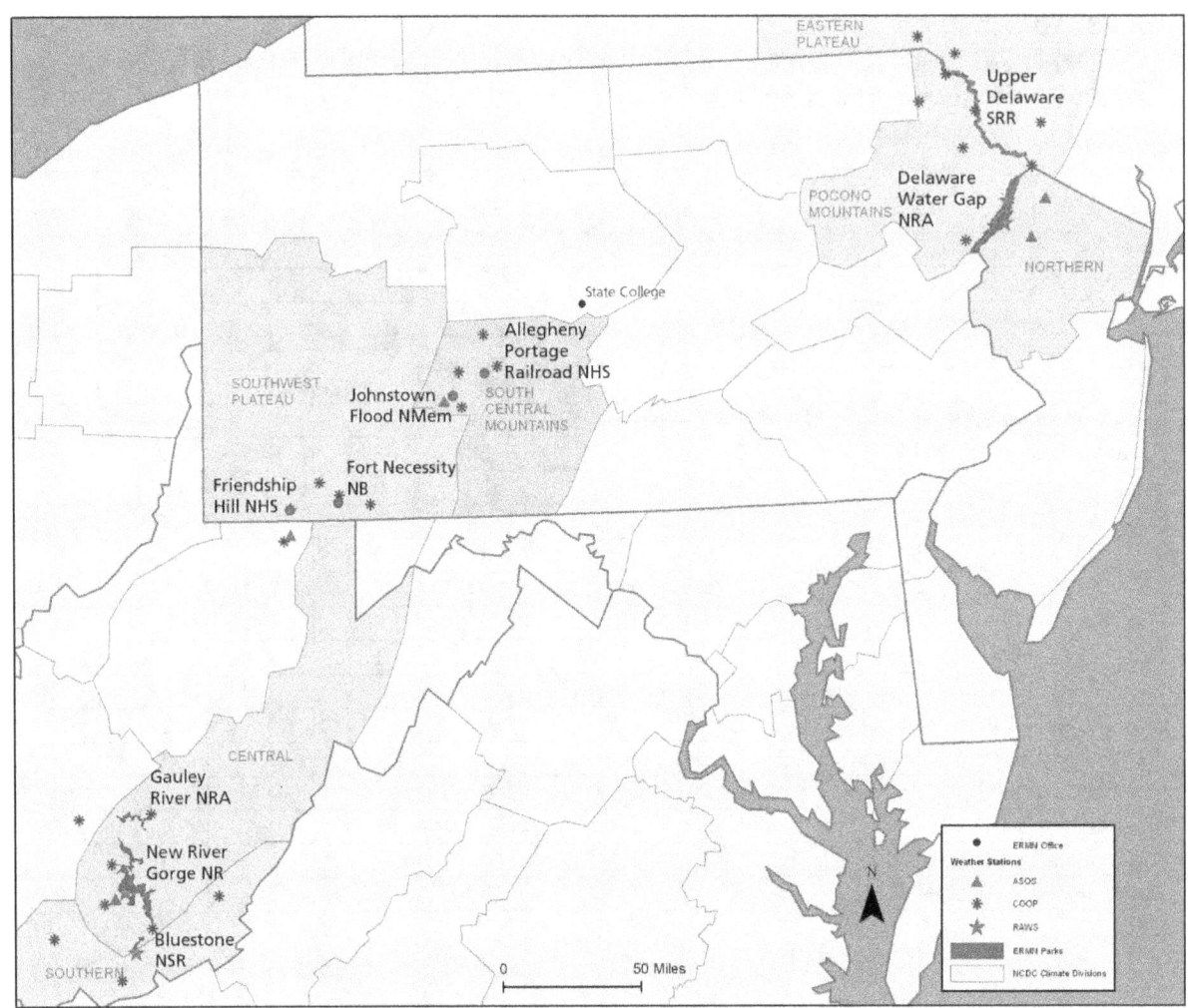

Figure 3. Location of stations selected for weather and climate monitoring and National Climatic Data Center (NCDC) climate divisions (which incorporate data from these and many other stations) that encompass parks in the Eastern Rivers and Mountains Network (ERMN). See Table 1 for definition of weather and climate observation network acronyms.

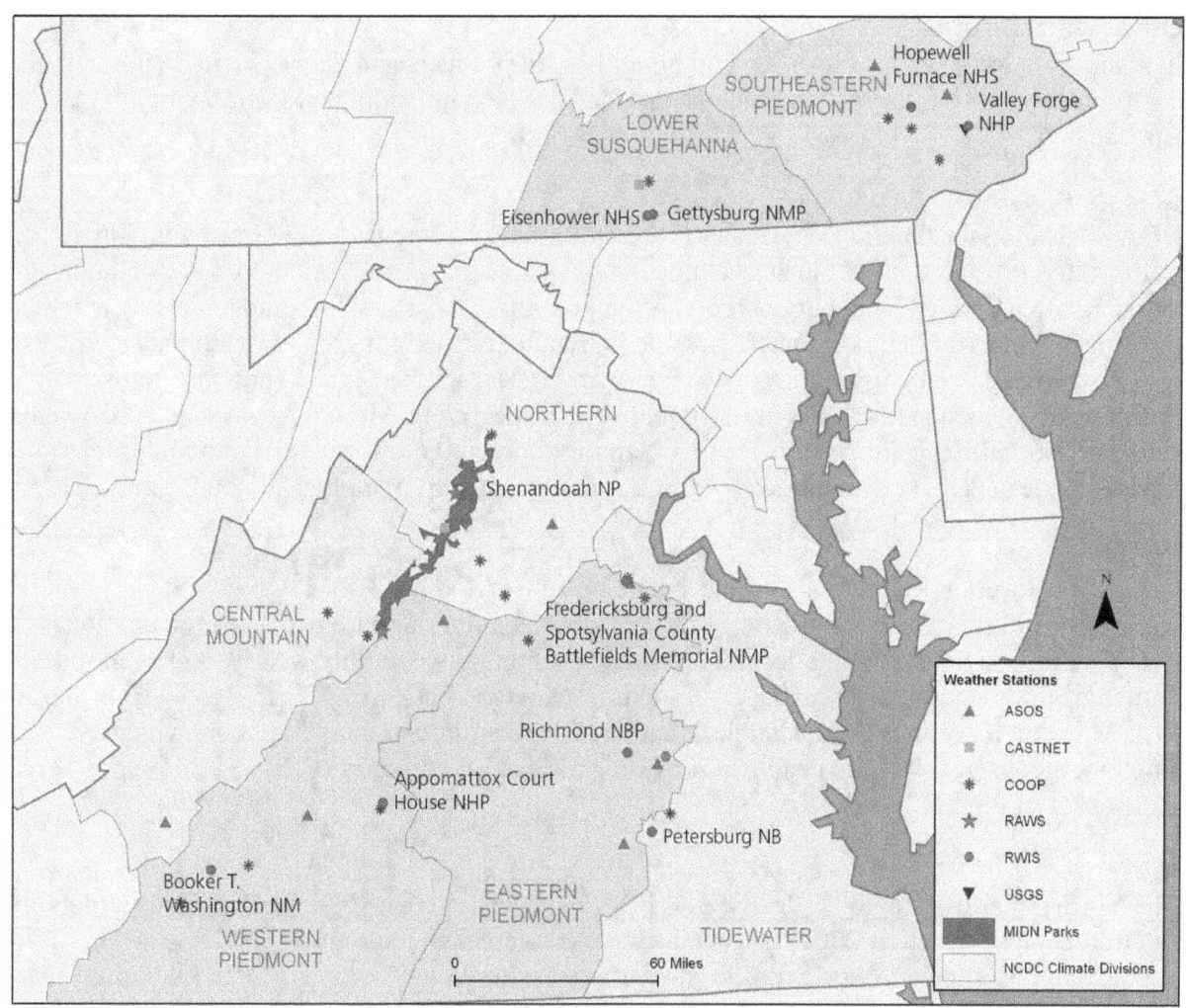

Figure 4. Location of stations selected for weather and climate monitoring and National Climatic Data Center (NCDC) climate divisions (which incorporate data from these and many other stations) that encompass parks in the Mid-Atlantic Network (MIDN). See Table 1 for definition of weather and climate observation network acronyms.

Other Data Sources

In addition to individual stations, several other derived products and datasets will be utilized in this protocol. A brief summary of each is provided below with additional information in Appendix A.

Climate Divisions

NOAA's National Climatic Data Center (NCDC) regularly aggregates data from individual stations into broader regions, such as climate divisions, using established methods. A climate division, often defined by county borders, is a region that is reasonably homogenous with respect to climatic and hydrologic characteristics and is frequently used for compiling climate statistics (http://www.esrl.noaa.gov/psd/data/usclimate/map.html). Figures 3 and 4 show the climate divisions that encompass ERMN and MIDN parks, respectively. Monthly, seasonal, and annual summaries of air temperature (minimum, maximum), precipitation, and the Palmer Drought Severity Index (PDSI) are compiled by climate division and are readily available from NCDC.

PRISM

Parameter-elevation Regressions on Independent Slopes Model (PRISM; Oregon State University 2007) is a climate mapping system that uses point measurements of precipitation, temperature, and other climatic factors to produce continuous, monthly, yearly, and event-based digital grid estimates at high spatial resolution. Data extend back to 1895. The greatest utility of PRISM is that it presents the spatial distribution of temperature and precipitation, which single-point observations are unable to provide. NPS is also currently (February 2011) a co-sponsor of PRISM.

NARR

The North American Regional Reanalysis (NARR) is generated at NOAA's National Centers for Environmental Prediction (NCEP). The objective is to create a long-term set of consistent climate data on a regional scale for the North American region. The NARR area (32 km grid spatial resolution) covers all of North and Central America and much of the flanking ocean regions. The period of the reanalysis is from October 1978 to the present and analyses were made eight times daily (at three-hour intervals). The numerous output variables include temperature, precipitation, soil moisture, snow cover, and snow depth.

Figure 5 shows average annual temperature (1979–2007) from three data sources (an individual COOP station, stations aggregated into a climate division, and the NARR dataset) we intend to utilize in this protocol representing the area around Upper Delaware SRR and Delaware Water Gap NRA. The agreement among datasets indicates that each is a good proxy depending on the analysis/reporting objective.

In addition to PRISM and NARR, we will also continue to evaluate two other gridded datasets for possible inclusion in the protocol and/or future analyses. The first is the Global Historical Climate Network (GHCN) and the second is the National Center for Atmospheric Research/National Center for Environmental Modeling Global Reanalysis Products (NCEP/NCAR GR). More information on both can be found at the following urls:
GHCN: http://www.ncdc.noaa.gov/ghcnm/
NCEP/NCAR GR: http://dss.ucar.edu/datasets/ds090.0/.

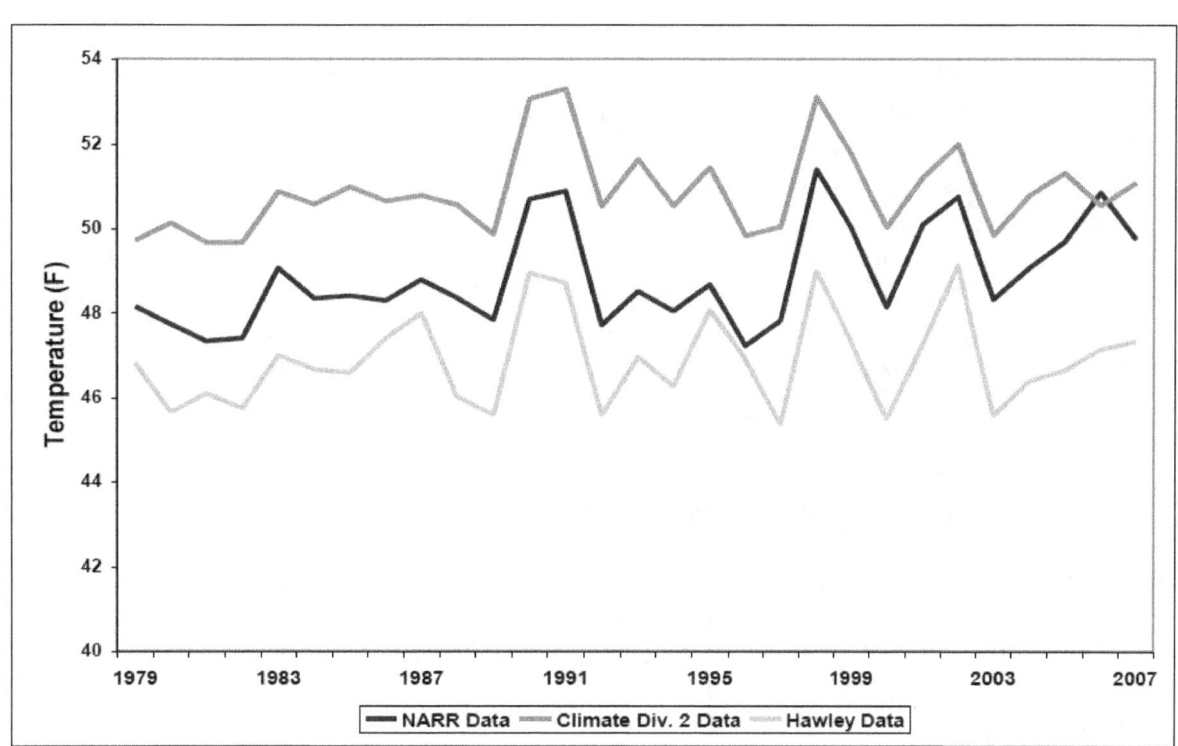

Figure 5. Estimates of average annual temperature for Upper Delaware SRR and Delaware Water Gap NRA derived from three data sources. The red line shows Pennsylvania Climate Division 2 "Pocono Mountains" data which is an aggregated summary of data from multiple stations in the Pennsylvania counties adjacent to the parks; the dark blue line is the temperature trend as derived from the NARR dataset centered within Delaware Water Gap NRA; and the light blue line shows the trend from a single COOP station at Hawley (HAWP1) near Upper Delaware SSR. The correlation coefficient between the NARR dataset and HAWP1 is 0.55. The correlation coefficient between the NARR dataset and the Climate Division 2 Data is 0.61.

Drought Indices

There are a number of drought indices used to estimate the severity of drought in an area using algorithms that incorporate recent temperature, rainfall, and soil moisture. The main indices included in this protocol are the Palmer Drought Severity Index (PDSI) and the United States Drought Monitor (DM) – Drought Intensity Index. The PDSI is a soil moisture algorithm incorporating precipitation and temperature data, as well as the local available water content of the soil. The values vary between extremely moist (>4.0) and extreme drought (<-4.0) with values between 2.0 and -2.0 near normal. The DM is a synthesis of multiple indices and impacts and represents a consensus of federal (U.S. Department of Agriculture [USDA] and NOAA) and academic scientists (National Drought Mitigation Center at University of Nebraska-Lincoln). The DM produces a summary map of drought intensity for the nation and all states each week. Intensity values range from 0 (abnormally dry) to 4 (exceptional drought).

Periodic Evaluation of the Sampling Design

We expect that stations will be added and removed from the sampling design over time as current stations become obsolete and/or new stations become active, among other reasons. Therefore, every three to five years we will review the sampling design, evaluate the spatial and temporal coverage provided by the available datasets/stations, and, as necessary, add and delete weather stations and acquire new data sources to ensure the best possible information is being used to meet the protocol objectives.

Field Methods

As previously described, this protocol relies exclusively on weather and climate monitoring programs and derived products administered by other agencies. As such, there is no "field" portion nor associated "field methods" required by ERMN or MIDN personnel. However, other NPS personnel do participate in the maintenance, calibration, operation, and data collection at some parks and stations (e.g., RAWS stations) under the guidance of the cooperating agency; details of which are not covered in this protocol. In this section, we provide an overview of the individual program operation, maintenance and inspection schedules, and where to find more information about the respective programs.

Observation Frequency, Details of Taking Measurements, and Recording

All stations included in the ERMN and MIDN protocol are operated year-round; however, observation frequency varies among the observing networks (Appendix A). Observer-based COOP stations require manual recording of climate observations on a daily basis. Daily observations are obtained by directly reading instruments (e.g., min-max thermometers), reading digital displays connected to electronic sensors, and manual measurements (e.g., using a snow stick to measure snow depth or rainfall amounts). These observations are reported daily (almost all values are entered electronically via the Web via "Weather Coder III") and/or monthly to climate data centers. The precipitation observations at USGS stream gauges are also daily values. All the other networks (RAWS, ASOS, RWIS, and CASTNet) are automated and record information hourly or sub-hourly (e.g., every 15–20 minutes). Data from the COOP, RAWS, and ASOS stations are automatically transmitted to regional and national climate data centers. Data from the USGS, CASTNet, and RWIS stations are maintained by the respective agencies/programs. Additional detail is provided in Appendix A.

Equipment Setup, Maintenance, Calibration, and Standards

Seasonal preparations and equipment setup are minimal, given that all stations are operated year round. Maintenance and calibration of climate stations tend to be the responsibility of external agencies. The following is a summary of individual program maintenance and inspection schedules and instrumentation standards for reference.

COOP

The NWS Observing Handbook No.2 details procedures for recording and reporting measurements from COOP stations. New observers are required to review this document as well as instructions for completing the recording and reporting datasheets. Additional training material is available at the COOP website: http://www.nws.noaa.gov/om/coop/training.htm.

Stations are established, supervised, and inspected by NWS personnel. Annual visits to cooperative stations are made for the purpose of observer training, equipment maintenance verification of station forms, and network integrity. In addition, each month the data are reviewed by the National Climate Data Center's quality assurance group. Procedures for the calibration and maintenance of equipment, reading instrumentation, and manual measurements are in the NWS Observing Handbook No. 2 (July 1989) provided at: http://www.nws.noaa.gov/om/coop/Publications/coophandbook2.pdf.

An updated (October 1996) procedure for measuring snow attributes is provided at: http://www.nws.noaa.gov/om/coop/snowguid.htm, with additional information provided in Doesken and Judson (1997).

Information on NWS equipment standards (summarized in Table 4) is provided at: http://www.weather.gov/directives/010/pd01013002d.pdf.

Table 4. COOP instrumentation standards.

Parameter	Accuracy	Range	Resolution
Air temperature (oF)	±2.0°F from -62 to -50°F ±1.0°F from -50 to +122°F ±2.0°F from +122 to +132°F	-62 to +132°F	0.1 °F
Liquid precipitation (in)	±0.02 in or 4% of hourly amount (whichever is greater)	<10 in/hr	0.01 in
Freezing precipitation (in)	Detection occurs whenever 0.01in accumulates	0–40 in	0.01 in
Frozen precipitation (water equivalent - in)	±0.04 in or 1% of total accumulation	0–40 in	0.01 in
Snow depth (in)	±0.1 in for depths 0–5 in ±1.0 in for depths >5–300 in	0–300 in	0.1 in

RAWS

Information on inspection, maintenance, and calibration for RAWS stations and other related documents are provided on the Interagency RAWS webpage (http://raws.fam.nwcg.gov/). Stations located within NPS boundaries are typically maintained by NPS fire management personnel and/or law enforcement rangers. The National Wildfire Coordinating Group (NWCG) published (August 2009) standards (summarized in Table 5) and standardized procedures for sensor performance, calibration, inspection, programming, and other matters related to the sound operation of RAWS stations. The document is provided at: http://raws.fam.nwcg.gov/standards/Weather_station_standards_rev08_2009_FINAL.pdf.

It is important to note that precipitation is measured using an unheated tipping bucket gauge which largely renders winter precipitation uninformative.

Training courses for weather station maintenance can also be taken; courses are announced on the RAWS website: http://raws.fam.nwcg.gov/training/2010training.html.

Table 5. RAWS instrumentation standards.

Parameter	Accuracy	Range	Resolution
Air temperature (°F)	±0.1°F	-58 to +140°F	Not specified
Relative humidity (%)	±2.0% from 0-80% at 20°C ±5.0% from 80-100% at 20°C	0-100%	Not specified
Precipitation (in)	Not specified	0-99.9 in	0.01 in
Wind speed (mph)	Not specified	0-150 mph	0.25 mph
Wind direction (degrees)	±2.0 degrees	0-359 degrees	1 degree
Solar radiation (W/m^2)	±5.0%	Not specified	Not specified
Fuel temperature (°F)	Not specified	-58 to +122°F	0.1°F
Fuel moisture (%)	10%	0-25 grams (water mass addition to 100g dowel)	Not specified

ASOS

Overall site maintenance and support is provided by the ASOS Automated Operations and Monitoring Center (AOMC). The ASOS User's Manual (March 1998), including information on site operation, documentation, maintenance, equipment standards (partial parameter list summarized in Table 6) is provided at: http://www.nws.noaa.gov/asos/pdfs/aum-toc.pdf and http://www.vaisala.com/Vaisala%20Documents/Technology%20Descriptions/Automated%20Weather%20Observation%20System%20Specifications%20FAA.pdf.

Table 6. ASOS instrumentation standards.

Parameter	Accuracy	Range	Resolution
Air temperature (°F)	±3.6°F from -80 to -58°F ±0.9°F from -58 to +122°F ±3.6°F from +122 to +130°F	-80 to +130°F	0.1°F
Dew point temperature (°F)	1.2°F dew point for bulb temp of +30 to +90°F (80% to 100% relative humidity) 2.3°F dew point for bulb temp of +30 to +120°F (15% to 75% relative humidity) 3.4°F dew point for bulb temp of -20 to +20°F (25% to 95% relative humidity)	-20 to +120°F	1.0°F
Precipitation (in)	±0.02 in or 4% of hourly total (whichever is greater)	0–10.0 in/hr	0.01 in
Wind speed (knots)	±2 knots or 5% (whichever is greater)	0–125 knots	1 knot
Wind direction (degrees)	±5.0 degrees when wind speed is ≥5 knots	0–359 degrees	1 degree
Atmospheric pressure (in of mercury)	±0.02 in of mercury	16.9–31.5 in of mercury	0.003 (recording) 0.005 (reporting)

CASTNet

Information on the inspection, maintenance, calibration, and instrumentation standards (summarized in Table 7) and related documents for CASTNet stations are provided in the quality assurance project plan (QAPP) revision 6 (November 2009) available at the EPA CASTNet website: http://epa.gov/castnet/javaweb/docs/qapp_v6_Main_Body.pdf.

Table 7. CASTNet instrumentation standards.

Parameter	Accuracy	Range	Resolution
Air temperature (°C)	±0.5°C	Not specified	Not specified
Relative humidity (%)	±10.0%	0–100%	Not specified
Precipitation (in)	±0.05 in†	Not specified	Not specified
Wind speed (m/s)	The greater of ± 0.5 m/s for winds <5 m/s or ± 5% for winds ≥5 m/s	Not specified	Not specified
Wind direction (degrees)	±5.0 degrees	1–360 degrees	Not specified
Solar radiation (W/m^2)	±10.0%	Not specified	Not specified
Ozone (%)	±10.0%	Not specified	Not specified

† For target value of 0.50 inch

RWIS

Overall site maintenance and support for RWIS instrumentation is the responsibility of that state's DOT (Department of Transportation). Within the ERMN and MIDN, the RWIS instrumentation is made by Vaisala. The specific standards of each instrument, summarized in Table 8, can be found at:

http://www.vaisala.com/en/roads/products/roadweathersystems/Pages/default.aspx.

Table 8. RWIS instrumentation standards.

Parameter	Accuracy	Range	Resolution
Air temperature (°C)	±0.3°C at 0°C, ±0.4C from -45.6 to +65.6°C	-45.6 to +65.6°C	Not specified
Relative humidity (%)	± 3% relative humidity at 70°F ± 5% From -45.6° C to +65.6° C	0 to 100%	Not specified
Precipitation (mm)	Not specified	Not specified	Not specified
Wind speed (m/s)	±0.3 m/s	0 to 100 m/s	Not specified
Wind direction (degrees)	±3 degrees	0-360°	Not specified

USGS

The USGS stream and rain monitoring network currently uses "tipping bucket rain gauges" for precipitation data. The specifics of the instrument's rainfall measurements, summarized in Table 9, can be found at: http://www.youngusa.com/products/3/18.html. Site maintenance is the responsibility of USGS.

Table 9. USGS instrumentation standards.

Parameter	Accuracy	Range	Resolution
Precipitation (mm)	2% up to 25 mm/hr 3% up to 50 mm/hr	Not specified	0.1 mm

End-of-Season Procedures

Since weather data are being collected continually, there is no "end of season." Procedures for downloading the data are addressed below and in more detail within the corresponding SOPs for each program.

Data Management

As described in the Operational Requirements chapter below, the weather and climate monitoring protocol will be implemented in collaboration with the Office of the Pennsylvania State Climatologist in the Department of Meteorology, Pennsylvania State University through a Cooperative Agreement. The Pennsylvania State Climatologist (PASC) is responsible for all aspects of data management including data acquisition, storage, additional quality assurance, and delivery of certified data to the NPS Network Data Managers. PASC already acquires and manages large volumes of weather and climate related data, including much of the data of interest to the ERMN and MIDN, as part of its ongoing activities and mission. This chapter provides an overview of the procedures for data acquisition, storage, certification, and archiving specific to the ERMN and MIDN. Additional details and context for this chapter may be found in the ERMN and MIDN Data Management Plans (Piekielek 2006, Callahan and Wakamiya 2009), which describe the overall information management strategy for the ERMN and MIDN.

Data Acquisition

PASC developed procedures to access observations (data) from the various weather and climate monitoring programs relevant to this protocol; each of which comes from a different data "stream." The ASOS data stream is gathered in real-time from the University Corporation for Atmospheric Research (UCAR) UNIDATA data service (NOAA Educational data feed; http://www.unidata.ucar.edu/) through a Local Data Manager (LDM) via a satellite data transmission. Pennsylvania State University Department of Meteorology is considered a Tier 1 site, meaning that its data acquisition has the highest priority since it then broadcasts/distributes the data to other UCAR partners in the Northeast and Middle Atlantic regions. COOP data are also acquired through the UNIDATA feed and are processed once a day. RAWS and CASTNET data streams are acquired through an ftp program that is programmed to run automatically every hour to retrieve data from respective programs via an anonymous ftp site. RWIS and USGS data are acquired in a similar fashion via scripts designed to "grab" data at regular intervals from publicly accessible websites.

Data Storage

All acquired data is then stored on a server (coda.met.psu.edu), housed, and managed by PASC. Data is stored in the MYSQL relational database management system. Data from each monitoring program (e.g., COOP, ASOS, RAWS, RWIS, USGS, etc.) are stored in a separate MYSQL database and can be accessed through an interactive data archive interface.

Quality Assurance

Each data stream has varying levels of associated quality assurance (from none to extensive). ASOS, RAWS, and CASTNet data have rigorous and extensive quality assurance beginning at the point of gather (data-logger on site) and at additional levels as described in the respective user's manuals and specification documents:

ASOS User's Manual (March 1998) available at: http://www.nws.noaa.gov/asos/pdfs/aum-toc.pdf.

RAWS standards (August 2009) available at: http://raws.fam.nwcg.gov/standards/Weather_station_standards_rev08_2009_FINAL.pdf.

Example RAWS quality assurance evaluation available at:
http://www.cefa.dri.edu/Publications/RAWSQCPhase1Report.pdf.

CASTNet quality assurance project plan (QAPP) revision 6 (November 2009) available at:
http://epa.gov/castnet/javaweb/docs/qapp_v6_Main_Body.pdf.

Example CASTNet quality assurance report available at:
http://epa.gov/castnet/javaweb/docs/QA_Quarterly_2010_Q3.pdf.

The COOP data quality control is now much more extensive in real-time as the electronically submitted data passes through several levels of quality assurance and is in a final format within a few days of submission. The finalized COOP data from NCDC replaces the daily data in the MYSQL database approximately twice a year (June and January). Only finalized COOP data is used for annual reporting. More information on COOP data quality assurance and performance monitoring is provided at the following urls:

http://www.ncdc.noaa.gov/oa/hofn/coop/coop-home.html
http://ams.confex.com/ams/pdfpapers/131217.pdf
http://journals.ametsoc.org/doi/pdf/10.1175/2010JAMC2375.1

Quality assurance of RWIS data is performed at the station through its datalogger, and additional quality assurance is performed by the current host company (Vaisala) after the data are received and processed in their database. More information is provided at:
http://www.vaisala.com/en/roads/products/roadweathersoftware/Pages/bureauservice.aspx.

Quality assurance of USGS precipitation data is performed manually by comparing rainfall amounts with nearby stations.

The Pennsylvania State Climate Office also runs a first level (*sensu* Durre et al. 2010) data quality assurance program on the FAA and COOP networks (checking for Tmin>Tmax and comparing daily values with known monthly extremes of maximum and minimum temperatures). Any egregious values are flagged and later checked manually.

Data Certification, Delivery, and Archiving

Data certification is a benchmark in the project information management process that indicates that: 1) the data are complete for the period of record; 2) they have undergone and passed the quality assurance checks; and 3) they are appropriately documented and in a condition for archiving, posting, and distribution as appropriate. Certification is not intended to imply that the data are completely free of errors or inconsistencies which may or may not have been detected during quality assurance reviews.

The PASC is responsible for data certification and delivery to the NPS ERMN Data Manager. At the time of writing (November 2011), the details of data certification and delivery are being established. The final process will be described in SOP 1 "Data Management." The intent is to have annual data (used for Annual Summary Reports) certified and delivered each year.

The certified data will be archived on the ERMN server which is secure and regularly backed-up.

Data Analysis and Reporting

The purpose of this chapter is to provide a framework and examples for routine data analysis and reporting for 1) annual status reports, 2) "Resource Briefs," and 3) periodic "variability and trends" reports.

Parks were organized for reporting purposes into logical groupings based primarily on geographic location and secondarily on management structure. For example, annual status reports for Allegheny Portage Railroad NHS and Johnstown Flood NMem will be grouped together into a single report given proximity to each other and the fact that they share a single natural resource manager. This also applies to Fort Necessity NB/Friendship Hill NHS and New River Gorge NR/Gauley River NRA/Bluestone NSR. Upper Delaware SRR and Delaware Water Gap NRA, while having distinct management structures, will be also be grouped together given close proximity to each other along the Delaware River. As such, there will be four annual reports for the ERMN.

A total of six annual reports will be produced for the MIDN following a similar rationale: individual reports for Shenandoah NP, Hopewell Furnace NHS/Valley Forge NHP, Eisenhower NHS/Gettysburg NMP, Richmond NBP/Petersburg NB, Appomattox Court House NHP/Booker T. Washington NM, and Fredericksburg and Spotsylvania NMP.

Purpose, Audience, and Timeline
The annual status report provides a summary and interpretation of the weather within and around park units for a single calendar year (January–December) for temperature, multiple forms of precipitation, drought, and several derived elements. The calendar year is also broken into component "seasons" which do not align precisely with a calendar year (Winter=December, January, February; Spring=March, April, May; Summer=June, July, August; Autumn=September, October, November). In addition to graphics and tabular summaries, status reports will contain a narrative that briefly summarizes the year's weather. The intent is not to be all inclusive of the data available, but to provide a succinct interpretation of the year's weather and place it in an appropriate historical and regional context (e.g., departures from normal/recent conditions). Status reports will generally not include discussion of trends, which will be covered in depth by the "variability and trend" reports. The primary audience for this report is ERMN personnel, MIDN personnel, and member-park natural resource management. It is likely that other researchers, collaborators, and interested parties, including the public, will also utilize these reports on occasion. Due to a lag-time in the availability of quality controlled and checked data, as well as the availability of derived products (e.g., PRISM maps), it is expected that these reports will be completed roughly six months after the end of the calendar year (i.e., by June). These reports will be peer-reviewed by at least the NPS lead (see Roles and Responsibilities section below) and respective park natural resource managers. The target outlet for the annual reports is the Natural Resource Program Center's Natural Resource Data Series (http://www.nature.nps.gov/publications/NRPM/).

Resource Briefs are short (1–4 pages) concise summaries of relevant information. They may be produced as an eye-catching executive summary of a longer report intended to reach audiences (e.g., Park Superintendents and other administrators) not inclined to read the full report. They may also be produced on a more immediate or timely topic for which a full report has not yet been produced. As such, Resource Briefs offer reporting flexibility both in timing and topic.

The periodic (5–10 year) "variability and trends" report will expand on the annual status reports and present thorough analyses of inter-annual variability and long-term historical trends for temperature, multiple forms of precipitation, drought, and several derived elements. The purpose is to provide scientifically-defensible analyses of variability and trends in a few weather/climate elements and to create high-quality datasets that can be used as covariate data in the analysis of other vital signs and/or park-based research projects and monitoring. The target audience is the same as for the annual reports, but because climate change is a high-profile, contentious topic, data quality control and peer review will be more extensive than that which occurs for the annual reports. Moreover, the target outlet for the variability and trends reports is the Natural Resource Program Center's Natural Resource Technical Report Series (http://www.nature.nps.gov/publications/NRPM/) which includes peer review and, preferably, a peer-reviewed scientific journal publication. All reports will have a record created in the NPS Natural Resource Information Portal (https://nrinfo.nps.gov/).

The following sections refer primarily to annual status reports. The framework for the "variability and trend" reports remains in development at the time of writing (November 2011). Excellent guidance and examples for developing scientifically sound trend reports can be found in Kittel (2008) and Kittel et al. (2009).

Gridded versus Point (Station) Data
In an attempt to meet the anticipated needs of a variety of park and network weather/climate data users, the reports will contain data summaries at multiple spatial scales: points (stations), climate divisions (aggregated station data), and larger regions (gridded or spatially continuous datasets such as PRISM or NARR). Station observations provide valuable information on the conditions at specific locations. Because stations have one of the longest histories of weather and climate data (often extending back to the late 19th century) they provide an essential dataset for understanding changes and trends in climate. Furthermore, because they are not modeled from any other dataset, they are the foundation of most other datasets. However, care should be taken when generalizing beyond the specific location of the station, especially when considering variables, such as precipitation, that show large local-scale variability. When attempting to generalize to large spatial scales, point-based observations are difficult to work with for the following reasons:

- Micro-scale climate – differences resulting from proximity to water, trees, vents, parking lots, walls, etc. that may affect representative measurements;

- Meso-scale climate – the location of the station relative to individual storm events, especially in summer when convective storms unevenly distribute rain;

- Data errors – errors related to the instrumentation or recording of the information; and

- Shortness and discontinuity of records – some stations do not have 30 years' worth of observations and/or have substantial data gaps.

To overcome the limitation of point (station) data, spatially continuous datasets (e.g., PRISM and NARR) that are regularly generated by climate scientists will also be utilized for our reporting needs. It is important to note that while these gridded datasets provide estimates of climate conditions at broad and continuous spatial scales, they are not necessarily representative of any specific point within a park and may smooth over or remove signals relevant to certain local processes.

Baselines for Comparison

The average value of a climate element over 30 years is defined as a climatological normal, which are calculated and established by NOAA's National Climatic Data Center (NCDC). Every ten years, NCDC computes new thirty-year climate normals for selected temperature and precipitation elements for a large number of U.S. climate and weather stations (ftp://ftp.ncdc.noaa.gov/pub/data/normals/1981-2010/documentation/temperature-methodology.pdf). The current (as of 2011) normals cover the period 1981–2010.

Whenever available, the 30-year normals established by NCDC will be used as the baseline for comparisons (e.g., departures from normal). In cases where data for the 30-year normal period are not available, we use alternative comparisons such as the new pseudo-normals from NCDC or a recent 10-year period. In some cases, sufficient data may simply not be available to calculate normals. For metrics that NCDC may not routinely calculate a normal, such as the number of days with more than 2 in (55 mm) of rain or liquid equivalent, normals will be calculated using the same time period (e.g., 1981–2010) as the current NCDC standard.

When comparing datasets (either by normal periods or other time scales), it should be noted that apparent changes in climate can be stemming from changes in instrumentation, exposure, or observing methodology. A change in the normal values does not (necessarily) imply a change in climate.

Weather Indicators

The annual status reports (and eventually the variability and trends reports) will summarize a series of what are termed temperature and precipitation "indicators" of climate change, defined as simple measures to quantify and track how (and if) temperature and precipitation patterns are changing over time. These 19 indicators include several means (e.g., average annual temperature), extremes (e.g., maximum temperature), and 11 derived elements (e.g., heavy precipitation days). The indicators selected are a subset of the many possible ways to summarize temperature and precipitation data and patterns and were selected largely because they (or similar ones) were utilized in two recent synthesis publications (Frumhoff et al. 2007, Karl et al. 2009). In short, the indicators try to capture, as simply as possible, how climate change and predicted future climate changes are altering local weather patterns. They are not necessarily tied to explicit ecological processes; but, instead, utilize simple benchmarks to document change. The indicators and how they are calculated are presented with example summary tables in the sections that follow.

Only a subset of the selected stations (one to three per park or park groupings) with longer periods of record, high data quality, and best reporting record (very little missing data) will be utilized for "indicator" analyses (see Sampling Design section above and Appendix D for the list of stations). This includes consideration of COOP stations that have been designated as United States Historical Climate Network (US HCN) sites (Appendix A).

Temperature is the most frequently used indicator of climate change and can be summarized in numerous ways. The ten temperature indicators tracked in the protocol are based on the observed increase in temperature (overall and extremes) throughout the Northeast and Mid-Atlantic since the 1970s and the predicted future changes (Frumhoff et al. 2007, Karl et al. 2009). Six of the ten indicators are different ways to describe changes in mean and extreme temperatures. Moreover, temperatures have increased (and are predicted to continue to increase) more dramatically during the winter (December, January, February) season. As such, three indicators are meant to document several ways (e.g., different benchmarks) winters, and winter nights (e.g., Sub-zero Nights), may be becoming "milder." The last indicator, growing season length, is the "frost-free" period during which plants grow most successfully, and is predicted to increase.

The ten temperature indicators are:

1. Average Annual Temperature: mean of 365 average daily temperatures (note: ASOS average daily temperatures are calculated by taking the average of 24 hourly average temperature values. For COOP and other station types the average daily temperature is calculated by taking mean of the daily maximum and the daily minimum temperature).

2. Average Annual Maximum Temperature: mean of 365 maximum daily temperatures.

3. Average Annual Minimum Temperature: mean of 365 minimum daily temperatures.

4. Maximum Temperature: highest recorded temperature during the calendar year; typically recorded during summer (June through August).

5. Minimum Temperature: lowest recorded temperature during the calendar year; typically recorded during winter (January through March).

6. Hot Days: number of days during the calendar year when the maximum daily temperature equals 90°F (32°C) or above.

7. Cold Days: number of days during the calendar year when the maximum daily temperature equals 32°F (0°C) or below.

8. Sub-freezing Days: number of days during the calendar year when the minimum daily temperature equals 32°F (0°C) or below; typically happens at night.

9. Sub-zero Days: number of days during the calendar year when the minimum daily temperature equals 0°F (-17.8°C) or below; typically happens at night.

10. Growing Season Length: number of days between the last spring "frost" (daily minimum temperature at or below 32°F (0°C)) and the first fall "frost."

Concurrent with overall increases in temperature, the Northeast and Mid-Atlantic have experienced changes in precipitation during the past several decades to a century (Frumhoff et al. 2007, Karl et al. 2009). Precipitation has been increasing in more northerly areas and decreasing in the southern areas; a pattern that is predicted to continue, and, perhaps more importantly, vary by season and by intensity (rainfall occurring in fewer, larger events). As such, five of the nine precipitation indicators tracked in the protocol attempt to describe and document these potential patterns. The remaining four indicators attempt to track patterns in snowfall.

The nine precipitation indicators are:

1. Annual Precipitation: cumulative yearly total liquid precipitation.

2. Seasonal Precipitation: cumulative seasonal (winter, spring, summer, autumn) total liquid precipitation.

3. Heavy Precipitation Days: number of days during the calendar year with ≥ 1.0 in (25 mm) liquid precipitation.

4. Extreme Precipitation Days: number of days during the calendar year with ≥ 2.0 in (51 mm) liquid precipitation.

5. Micro-drought: number of strings of seven or more consecutive days during the calendar year without a trace ($<.01$ in / 0.3 cm) of liquid precipitation.

6. Annual Snowfall: cumulative yearly total snowfall.

7. Measurable Snow Days: number of days during the calendar year with measurable (≥ 0.1 in [0.3 cm]) snow.

8. Moderate Snow Days: number of days during the calendar year with ≥ 3.0 in (7.6 cm) of snow.

9. Heavy Snow Days: number of days during the calendar year with ≥ 5.0 in (12.7 cm) of snow.

Internet-based Mapping and Data Portal

The Pennsylvania Station Climatologist has developed and maintains an Internet-based mapping portal enabling access to station data in near-real time. The portal provides a map of relevant stations for each park. After selecting a station from the map interface, the user can view station metadata, current and historical data, and data summaries and graphics, and query and download data in multiple formats. It is important to note that these data should be considered provisional when used in near-real time (e.g., when viewed or downloaded from the portal). The provisional period includes all data acquired in the prior six months (after which the data available through the portal are replaced with full quality controlled data from NCDC). The interface is accessible via the following url: http://climate.met.psu.edu/gmaps/NPS_DEVELOPMENT/interface.php

An instruction manual or "tutorial" was also developed to help users navigate the portal as well as understand and utilize its many features. The tutorial is available at the following url: http://climate.met.psu.edu/gmaps/NPS_DEVELOPMENT/NPStutorial.2.26.08.pdf.

Both urls are also accessible through the ERMN and MIDN websites.

Status Report Content

Each annual status report will contain the following sections. Additional information can be included at the authors' discretion or at the request of park resource managers; however, the intent is to include the following at a minimum.

Annual status reports will include the components described below and present both English (°F and inches) and metric units (°C, millimeters, and centimeters for snow).

Overview of Stations

Each annual status report will provide a map of the pertinent stations relative to the park boundary (Figure 6) and a table with the station name, brief metadata (e.g., period of record, observing network), and a summary of data completeness for the stations utilized in that year's report (Table 10). All stations selected to be representative of the weather and climate of each park (see Sampling Design section) will be included in the overview.

Temperature: Point (Station) Summary

In addition to a short narrative summarizing temperature patterns during the past calendar year, tables of station-specific annual and monthly average temperature (Table 11) and annual and monthly departures from that station's 30-year normal (Table 12) will be presented. The intent is to provide an informative summary and quick reference location for the past calendar year at an intermediate temporal scale (e.g., monthly instead of daily). Contrasting the current year's averages with the 30-year normal will help put the data in historical perspective. Presenting data for all selected stations allows the variability among stations to be available to end users.

When more than 10% of the data (greater than three days in a month) are missing, the entire month's data are listed as missing (M).

All stations selected to be representative of the weather and climate of each park (see Sampling Design section) will be included in the Temperature – Point (Station) Summary.

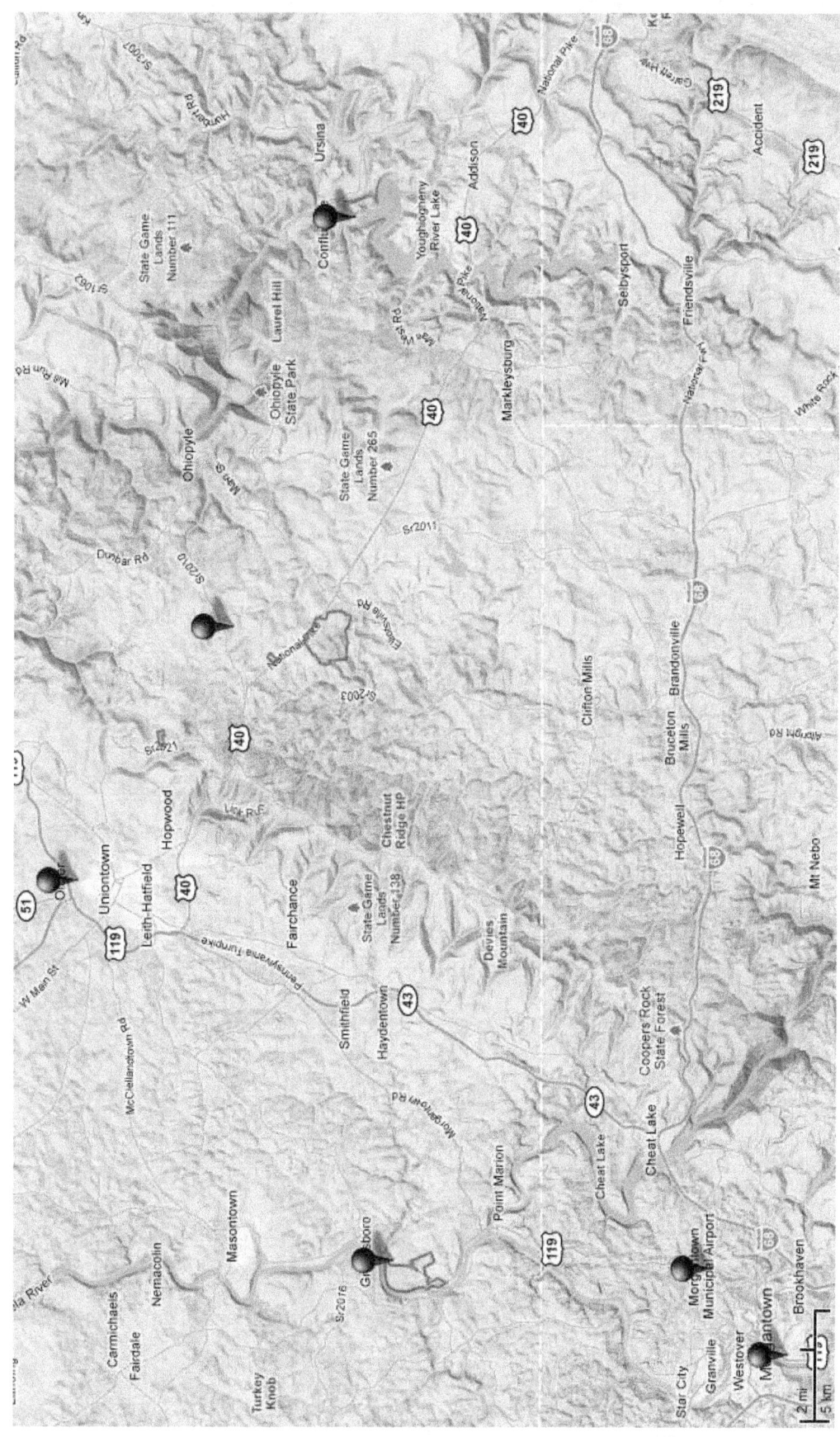

Figure 6. Example map showing the location of the six stations used in the 2009 annual weather and climate status report for Fort Necessity NB and Friendship Hill NHS.

Table 10. Example table showing the station name, observing network, data period of record, and data completeness summary for the six stations used in the 2009 annual weather and climate status report for Fort Necessity NB and Friendship Hill NHS.

Station	Observing Network	Station Name	Period of Record (POR)		Percentage of Time Reporting Temperature for 2009	Percentage of Time Reporting Precipitation for 2009	Percentage of Time Reporting Temperature for entire POR	Percentage of Time Reporting Precipitation for entire POR
CHKP1	COOP	Chalk Hill 2 ENE	07/01/1977	Present	100.0	98.6	99.9	99.9
GYLP1	COOP	Grays Landing	10/01/1996	Present	100.0	100.0	94.2	98.3
UNTP1	COOP	Uniontown 1 NE	01/01/1894	Present	100.0	99.5	97.3	95.6
CONP1	COOP	Confluence	07/01/1946	Present	100.0	99.5	99.7	99.7
MOEW2	COOP	Morgantown Lock and Dam	09/01/1921	Present	99.7	99.7	97.4*	96.1
KMGW	FAA	Morgantown Airport	12/31/1973	Present	100.0	100.0	99.0	99.0

* Percentage of time reporting temperature for Morgantown Lock and Dam is based upon a period of record beginning on 06/01/1944. This station did not report temperature prior to this date.

Table 11. Example table showing a summary of annual and monthly average temperatures for the six stations used in the 2009 annual weather and climate status report for Fort Necessity NB and Friendship Hill NHS.

Station Name	Station	Jan	Feb	Mar	Apr	May	Jun	Jul	Aug	Sep	Oct	Nov	Dec	Annual
Morgantown Airport	KMGW	26.9°F	34.2°F	44.8°F	52.9°F	62.3°F	68.8°F	70.3°F	74.3°F	67.0°F	54.0°F	50.2°F	34.2°F	53.3°F
		-2.8°C	1.2°C	7.1°C	11.6°C	16.8°C	20.4°C	21.3°C	23.5°C	19.5°C	12.2°C	10.1°C	1.2°C	13.2°C
Chalk Hill 2 ENE	CHKP1	19.5°F	26.4°F	37.0°F	46.2°F	56.4°F	61.8°F	62.5°F	66.4°F	59.2°F	45.7°F	43.5°F	26.1°F	45.9°F
		-7.0°C	-3.1°C	2.8°C	7.9°C	13.6°C	16.6°C	17°C	19.1°C	15.1°C	7.6°C	6.4°C	-3.3°C	11.8°C
Uniontown 1 NE	UNTP1	25.4°F	32.6°F	42.1°F	50.9°F	61.5°F	67.5°F	68.5°F	72.3°F	65.4°F	50.6°F	48.9°F	31.4°F	51.4°F
		-3.7°C	0.3°C	5.6°C	10.5°C	16.4°C	19.7°C	20.3°C	22.4°C	18.6°C	10.3°C	9.4°C	-0.3°C	13.4°C
Confluence	CONP1	21.6°F	29.7°F	39.0°F	47.5°F	58.7°F	64.8°F	66.1°F	70.2°F	62.0°F	48.1°F	45.6°F	28.9°F	48.5°F
		-5.8°C	-1.3°C	3.9°C	8.6°C	14.8°C	18.2°C	19.0°C	21.2°C	16.6°C	9.0°C	7.5°C	-1.7°C	13.2°C
Morgantown Lock and Dam	MOEW2	25.2°F	31.8°F	42.1°F	50.5°F	61.1°F	67.6°F	68.7°F	72.1°F	64.9°F	51.1°F	47.7°F	32.7°F	51.3°F
		-3.8°C	-0.1°C	5.6°C	10.3°C	16.2°C	19.8°C	20.4°C	22.3°C	18.3°C	10.6°C	8.7°C	0.4°C	13.3°C
Grays Landing	GYLP1	25.0°F	31.8°F	41.3°F	48.9°F	59.9°F	M	67.8°F	71.9°F	64.3°F	50.3°F	47.0°F	30.4°F	M
		-3.9°C	-0.1°C	5.2°C	9.4°C	15.5°C	M	19.9°C	22.2°C	17.9°C	10.2°C	8.3°C	-0.9°C	M

M = missing data (Monthly statistics are reported as 'M' if greater than 4 days of data are missing).

Table 12. Example table showing a summary of annual and monthly departures from the 30-year (1971–2000) normal temperature for the six stations used in the 2009 annual weather and climate status report for Fort Necessity NB and Friendship Hill NHS.

Station name	Station	Jan	Feb	Mar	Apr	May	Jun	Jul	Aug	Sep	Oct	Nov	Dec	Annual
Chalk Hill 2 ENE	CHKP1	-6.6°F	-2.7°F	-0.9°F	-1.9°F	-0.9°F	-3.1°F	-6.1°F	-0.8°F	-1.3°F	-4.3°F	3.5°F	-4.7°F	-2.5°F
		-3.7°C	-1.5°C	-0.5°C	-1.1°C	-0.5°C	-1.7°C	-3.4°C	-0.4°C	-0.7°C	-2.4°C	1.9°C	-2.6°C	-1.4°C
Grays Landing*	GYLP1	-3.9°F	0.4°F	1.5°F	-0.5°F	0.5°F	M	-4.3°F	1.4°F	0.6°F	-1.7°F	4.5°F	-3.3°F	M
		-2.2°C	0.2°C	0.8°C	-0.3°C	0.3°C	M	-2.4°C	0.8°C	0.3°C	-0.9°C	2.5°C	-1.8°C	M
Uniontown 1 NE	UNTP1	-3.5°F	1.2°F	2.3°F	1.5°F	2.1°F	-0.5°F	-3.6°F	1.8°F	1.7°F	-1.4°F	6.4°F	-2.3°F	0.5°F
		-1.9°C	0.7°C	1.3°C	0.8°C	1.2°C	-0.3°C	-2.0°C	1.0°C	0.9°C	-0.8°C	3.6°C	-1.3°C	0.3°C
Confluence	CONP1	-5.0°F	0.4°F	0.9°F	-0.9°F	0.2°F	-2.4°F	-5.2°F	0.0°F	-1.1°F	-3.2°F	4.8°F	-2.3°F	-1.2°F
		-2.8°C	0.2°C	0.5°C	-0.5°C	0.1°C	-1.3°C	-2.9°C	0.0°C	-0.6°C	-1.8°C	2.7°C	-1.3°C	-0.7°C
Morgantown Lock and Dam	MOEW2	-5.6°F	-1.9°F	0.5°F	-1.8°F	0.2°F	-1.8°F	-4.9°F	0.0°F	-0.9°F	-3.3°F	3.4°F	-2.7°F	-1.6°F
		-3.1°C	-1.1°C	0.3°C	-1.0°C	0.1°C	-1.0°C	-2.7°C	0.0°C	-0.5°C	-1.8°C	1.9°C	-1.5°C	-0.9°C
Morgantown Airport	KMGW	-3.5°F	0.7°F	2.5°F	1.0°F	1.1°F	-0.3°F	-2.9°F	2.4°F	1.7°F	-0.2°F	5.9°F	-0.8°F	0.6°F
		-1.9°C	0.4°C	1.4°C	0.6°C	0.6°C	-0.2°C	-1.6°C	1.3°C	0.9°C	-0.1°C	3.3°C	-0.4°C	0.3°C

M = missing data (Monthly statistics are reported as 'M' if greater than 4 days of data are missing).

*Indicates a station's period of record is less than 30 years. In these cases, the departure from normal values were calculated with normals derived from data spanning the length of the station's period of record. Stations with a period of record of less than 5 years were not included in this table.

Temperature: Spatial Summary

The PRISM gridded dataset will be utilized to augment the station data (above) by providing a spatially continuous figure for monthly maximum and minimum temperature anomalies. Figure 7 shows an example of departures from monthly maximum temperature; a similar figure is available (but not shown) for departures from monthly minimum temperatures. These data and figures are generated by and readily available from the PRISM group at Oregon State University (Appendix A). It was determined by the authors that a presentation of monthly temperature anomalies (departures from the 30-year normal) was a sufficient "spatial summary" as opposed to also presenting actual temperature values.

Temperature: Indicators

The ten "temperature indicators" defined above will be presented in tabular format (Table 13) along with the 30-year normal for each indicator. Pairing the past calendar year value with the 30-year normal helps readers evaluate "current status" by providing historical context. Long-term trends will be analyzed and presented in periodic "variability and trends" reports.

Temperature and Precipitation: Rankings

The National Oceanic and Atmospheric Administration provides monthly, seasonal, and annual rankings for temperature and precipitation for regions including states and climate divisions. These rankings extend back 115 years as of 2009 (117 years as of 2011 and so on) and provide a valuable and informative way to place a particular calendar year and its component seasons in historic context. Each annual report will provide these rankings for relevant climate divisions (Table 14). The rankings are also accessible directly from NOAA at the following website: http://lwf.ncdc.noaa.gov/temp-and-precip/ranks.php.

Precipitation: Point (Station) Summary

In addition to a short narrative summarizing precipitation patterns during the past calendar year, tables of station-specific annual and monthly total precipitation (Table 15) and annual and monthly departures from each station's 30-year normal (Table 16) will be presented. The intent is to provide an informative summary and quick reference location for the past calendar year at an intermediate temporal scale (e.g., monthly instead of daily). Contrasting the current year's averages with the 30-year normal will help put the data in historical perspective. Presenting data for all selected stations allows the variability among stations to be available to end users.

All stations selected to be representative of the weather and climate of each park (see Sampling Design section) will be included in the Precipitation – Point (Station) Summary.

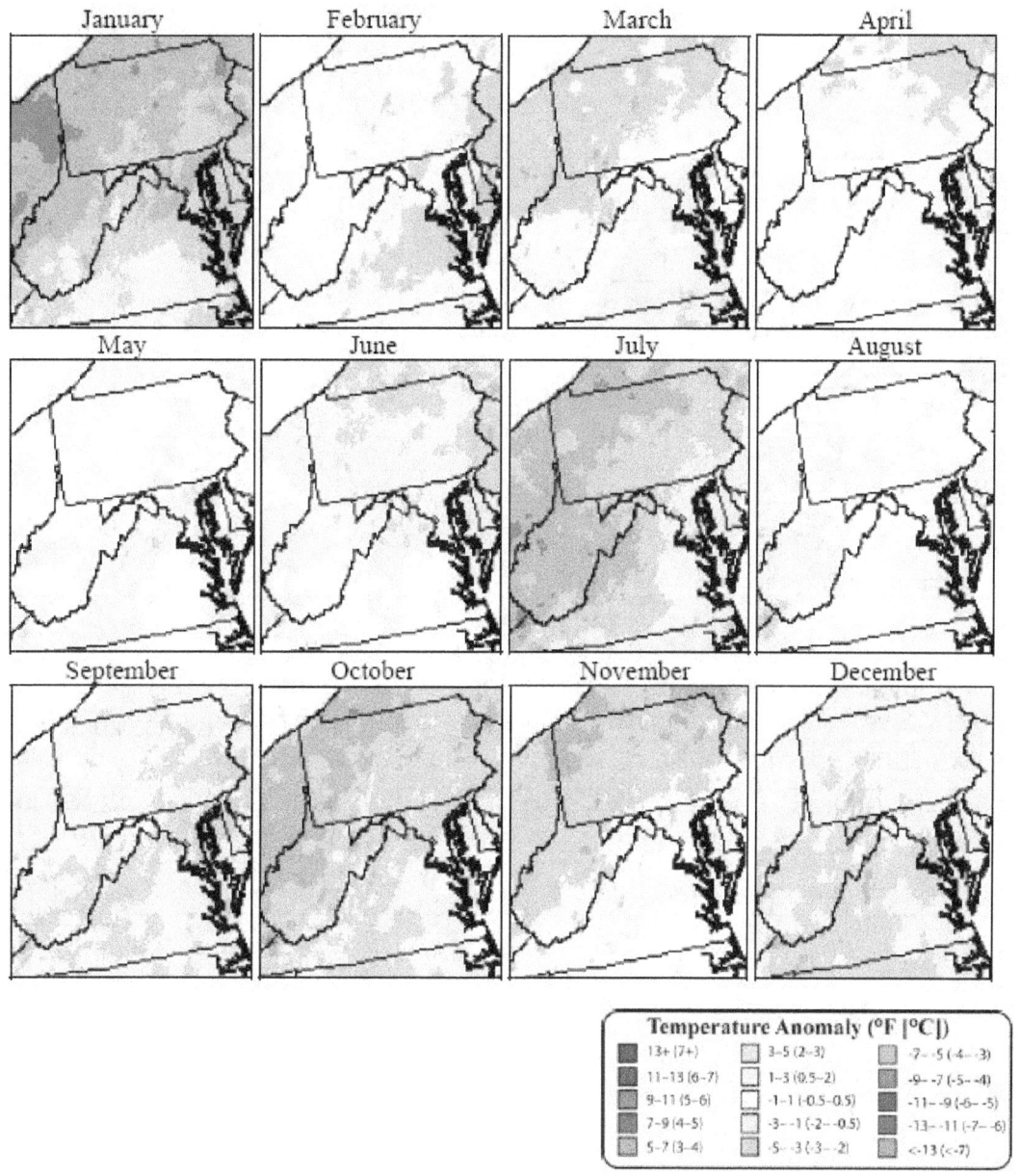

Figure 7. Example maps showing 2009 departure from average monthly maximum temperature compared to the 30-year normal (1971–2000) for the region spanning ERMN and MIDN parks.

Table 13. Example table showing the status of 2009 temperature indicators compared to the 30-year normal (1971–2000) at the Chalk Hill (CHKP1) and Morgantown Lock and Dam (MOEW2) stations used in the 2009 annual weather and climate status report for Fort Necessity NB and Friendship Hill NHS.

Temperature Indicator	CHKP1 2009	CHKP1 1971–2000	MOEW2 2009	MOEW2 1971–2000
Average Annual Temperature	45.9°F 7.7°C	48.4°F 9.1°C	51.3°F 10.7°C	52.9°F 11.6°C
Average Annual Maximum Temperature	56.6°F 13.7°C	58.5°F 14.7°C	61.6°F 16.4	63.5°F 17.5°C
Maximum Temperature	86.0°F 30.0°C	87.3°F 30.7°C	90.0°F 32.2°C	93.3°F 34.1°C
Hot Days (days with Tmax≥90°F/32°C)	0	1	1	8
Average Annual Minimum Temperature	35.2°F 1.8°C	39.2°F 4.0°C	41.1°F 5.1°C	41.8°F 5.4°C
Minimum Temperature	-23.0°F -30.6°C	-11.0°F -23.9°C	-4.0°F -20.0°C	-4.4°F -20.2
Cold Days (days with Tmax≤32°F/0°F)	50	40	32	22
Sub-freezing Days (days with Tmin≤32°F/0°C)	152	133	116	116
Sub-zero Days (days with Tmin≤0°F/-17.8°C)	10	7	3	3
Growing Season Length (days between last spring 32°F/0°C and first fall 32°F/0°C)	139	145	189	172

Table 14. Example table showing the seasonal temperature and precipitation rankings over the past 115 years (1 = warmest/wettest year and 115 = coldest/driest year) for Pennsylvania Climate Division 9.

PA Climate Division 9 Rankings "Southwest Plateau"	Jan–Feb–Mar WINTER	Apr–May–Jun SPRING	Jul–Aug–Sep SUMMER	Oct–Nov–Dec AUTUMN
Temperature-2009	72	68	104	63
Precipitation-2009	94	31	73	44

Table 15. Example table showing a summary of annual and monthly total liquid precipitation for the six stations used in the 2009 annual weather and climate status report for Fort Necessity NB and Friendship Hill NHS.

Station name	Station	Jan	Feb	Mar	Apr	May	Jun	Jul	Aug	Sep	Oct	Nov	Dec	Annual
Morgantown Airport, WV	KMGW	2.8 in	1.8 in	1.7 in	3.8 in	6.3 in	4.6 in	3.3 in	3.7 in	2.6 in	3.9 in	1.0 in	3.2 in	38.7 in
		72 mm	46 mm	43 mm	96 mm	161 mm	117 mm	84 mm	94 mm	66 mm	98 mm	25 mm	81 mm	983 mm
Cha k Hill, PA	CHKP1	4.7 in	3.6 in	2.4 in	4.3 in	7.1 in	4.9 in	3.2 in	4.7 in	3.4 in	6.1 in	1.6 in	4.6 in	50.6 in
		120 mm	91 mm	60 mm	110 mm	181 mm	125 mm	82 mm	119 mm	86 mm	155 mm	40 mm	117 mm	1,285 mm
Uniontown, PA	UNTP1	3.4 in	1.7 in	2.0 in	3.0 in	6.0 in	2.8 in	3.3 in	3.1 in	2.2 in	4.5 in	1.2 in	3.3 in	36.5 in
		87 mm	44 mm	50 mm	76 mm	153 mm	70 mm	85 mm	79 mm	55 mm	134 mm	30 mm	84 mm	927 mm
Confluence, PA	CONP1	3.8 in	2.0 in	1.2 in	3.6 in	5.6 in	7.0 in	3.7 in	3.5 in	2.0 in	5.9 in	1.2 in	4.7 in	44.3 in
		98 mm	50 mm	30 mm	90 mm	143 mm	178 mm	95 mm	89 mm	51 mm	150 mm	31 mm	119 mm	1,125 mm
Morgantown Lock and Dam, WV	MOEW2	4.0 in	2.0 in	1.7 in	4.1 in	7.1 in	4.6 in	2.9 in	4.4 in	2.6in	3.8 in	0.9 in	3.7 in	41.7 in
		101 mm	50 mm	44 mm	105 mm	181 mm	117 mm	73 mm	111 mm	65 mm	95 mm	23 mm	95 mm	1,059 mm
Grays Landing, PA	GYLP1	3.1 in	1.4 in	2.0 in	3.7 in	9.0 in	M	2.9 in	3.7 in	2.0 in	4.6 in	0.8 in	3.7 in	M
		79 mm	35 mm	50 mm	93 mm	228 mm	M	73 mm	95 mm	51 mm	116 mm	20 mm	93 mm	M

M = missing data (Monthly statistics are reported as 'M' if greater than 4 days of data are missing).

Table 16. Example table showing a summary of annual and monthly percent of 30-year (1971-2000) normal liquid precipitation for the six stations used in the 2009 annual weather and climate status report for Fort Necessity NB and Friendship Hill NHS.

Station name	Station	Jan	Feb	Mar	Apr	May	Jun	Jul	Aug	Sep	Oct	Nov	Dec	Annual
Morgantown Airport, WV	KMGW	98	67	46	107	152	112	78	92	74	136	30	103	91
Chalk Hill, PA	CHKP1	109	95	50	86	136	103	58	110	75	167	37	113	95
Uniontown, PA	UNTP1	115	62	54	80	138	64	72	79	60	155	34	107	85
Confluence, PA	CONP1	109	67	31	90	126	175	78	94	50	197	33	134	98
Morgantown Lock and Dam, WV	MOEW2	122	68	45	112	163	114	68	110	76	131	25	115	96
Grays Landing, PA	GYLP1	97	59	53	100	209	M	72	103	70	187	24	131	M

M = missing data (Monthly statistics are reported as 'M' if greater than 4 days of data are missing).

*Indicates a station's period of record is less than 30 years. In these cases, the departure from normal values was calculated with normals derived from data spanning the length of the station's period of record. Stations with a period of record of less than 5 years were not included in this table.

Precipitation: Spatial Summary

The PRISM gridded dataset will be utilized to augment the station data (above) by providing a spatially continuous figure (Figure 8) for monthly total precipitation anomalies. These data and figures are generated by and readily available from the PRISM group at Oregon State University (Appendix A). It was determined that a presentation of monthly precipitation anomalies (departures from the 30-year normal) was a sufficient "spatial summary" as opposed to also presenting monthly total values. Since the PRISM data sets have been quality assured by most state climate offices for their representation of significant elevation effects, these data sets are considered a valuable auxiliary representation of anomalies.

Precipitation: Indicators

The nine "precipitation indicators" defined above will be presented in tabular format (Table 17) along with the 30-year normal for each indicator. Pairing the past calendar year value with the 30-year normal helps readers evaluate "current status" by providing historical context. Long-term trends will be analyzed and presented in periodic "variability and trends" reports.

Drought Status

There are a number of drought indices used to estimate the severity of drought in an area using algorithms that incorporate recent temperatures, rainfall, and soil moisture. The main indices included in this protocol are the Palmer Drought Severity Index (PDSI) and the Drought Monitor (DM) – Drought Intensity Index. Both indices are generated by external agencies (Appendix A) and will be summarized by climate division, state, and region as appropriate (e.g., Figure 9).

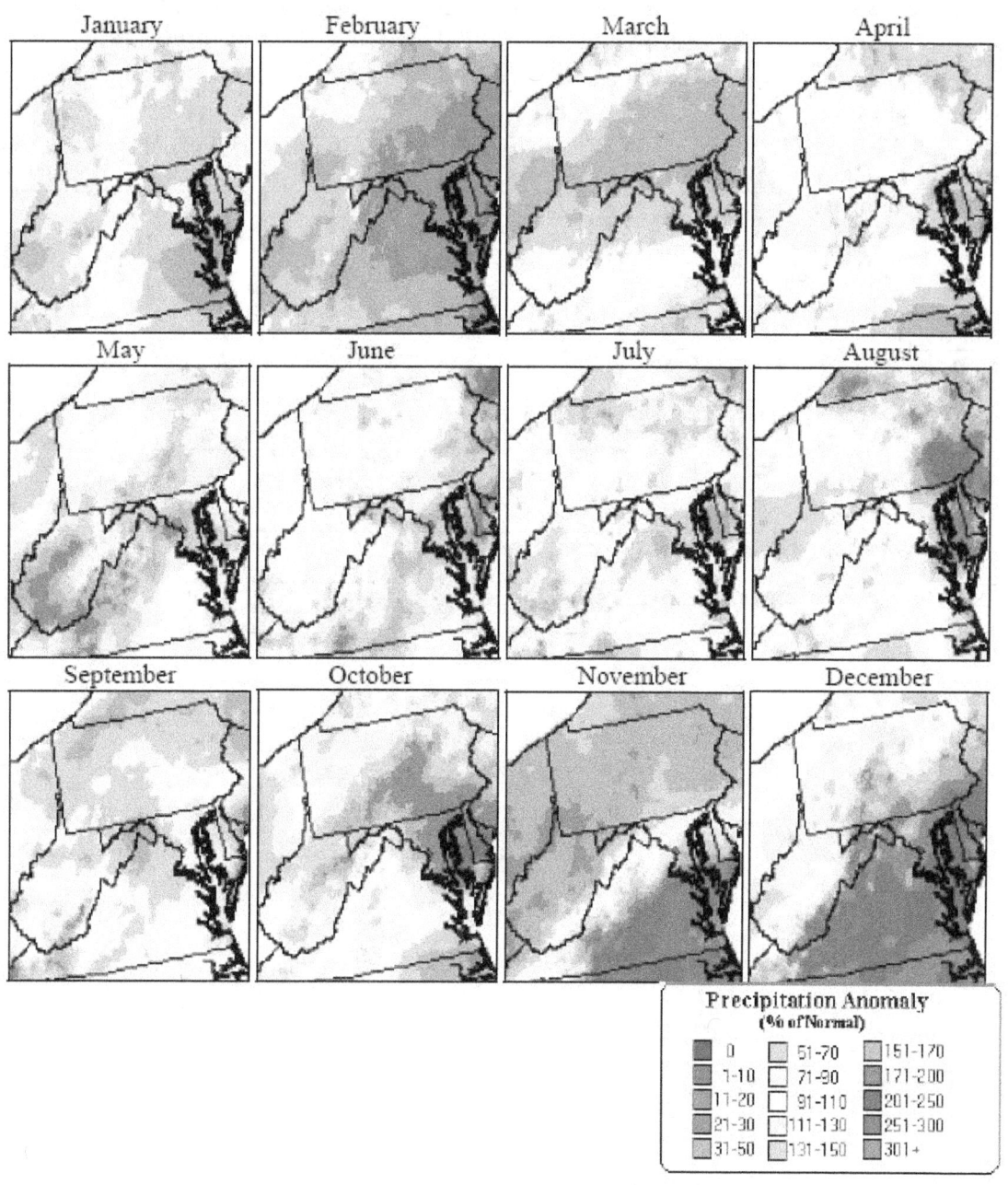

Figure 8. Example map showing 2009 percent of monthly 30-year normal (1971–2000) total liquid precipitation compared for the region spanning ERMN and MIDN parks.

Table 17. Example table showing the status of 2009 precipitation indicators compared to the 30-year normal (1971–2000) at the Chalk Hill (CHKP1) and Morgantown Lock and Dam (MOEW2) stations used in the 2009 annual status report for Fort Necessity NB and Friendship Hill NHS.

Precipitation Indicator	CHKP1 2009	CHKP1 1971–2000	MOEW2 2009	MOEW2 1971–2000
Annual Precipitation	50.6 in 1,285.2 mm	54.7 in 1,389.4 mm	41.7 in 1,059.2	42.1 in 1,069.3 mm
Autumn (Oct, Nov, Dec) Precipitation	12.3 in 312.4 mm	12.2 in 309.9 mm	8.4 in 213.4 mm	9.7 in 246.4 mm
Heavy Precipitation Days (days with ≥1.0 in (25 mm) liquid precipitation)	8	11	6	8
Extreme Precipitation Days (days with ≥2.0 in (51 mm) liquid precipitation)	1	1	1	1
Micro-drought (strings of 7+ days without liquid precipitation n)	5	3	7	6
Annual Snowfall	74.9 in 1,902.5 mm	88.7 in 2,253.0 mm	18.6 in 472.4 mm	22.6 in 574.0 mm
Snow Days (days with ≥0.1 in (0.3 cm) snow)	51	54	23	19
Moderate Snow Days (days with ≥2.0 in (5.0 cm) snow)	14	17	2	3
Heavy Snow Days (days with ≥5.0 in (12.7 cm) snow)	4	4	0	1

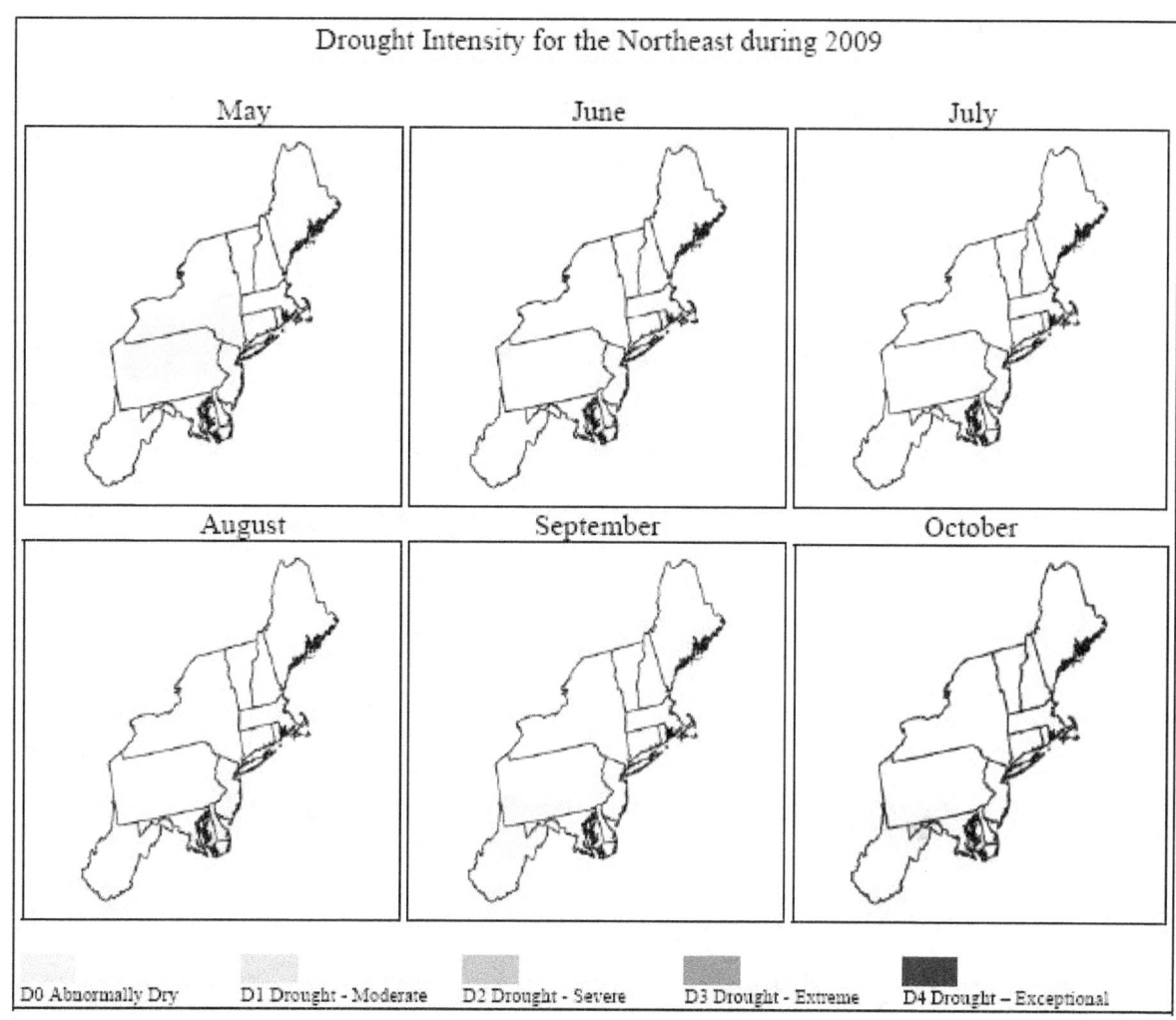

Figure 9. Example map showing 2009 mid-month United States Drought Monitor – Drought Intensity Index values for the Northeast.

Operational Requirements

This chapter describes the personnel, funding resources, roles, and responsibilities required to implement the weather and climate monitoring protocol. The ERMN and MIDN share resources equally (personnel and monetary) required to implement this protocol and, as such, the protocol can be easily modified should either network decide to discontinue participation in the protocol in the future.

Personnel Requirements

The weather and climate monitoring protocol will be implemented in collaboration with the Office of the Pennsylvania State Climatologist through a Cooperative Agreement. The Pennsylvania State Climatologist (PASC) will be the project lead. The project lead plans and coordinates project operations, namely the acquisition, analysis, and reporting of weather and climate data. Each I&M Network Program Manager will be a NPS lead who is responsible for protocol oversight and administration (e.g., maintaining the Cooperative Agreement), coordination with the project lead, and communication with NPS resource managers and other interested parties. The NPS lead will also assist the project lead with the conception and writing of reports at times and will always review reports and data delivered by the project lead. The NPS lead will coordinate additional peer-review as required in conjunction with the Northeast Regional I&M Program Manager. The network data managers will advise on data management activities throughout and annually receive final, certified, data products from the project lead for archiving on NPS servers.

General roles and responsibilities for this protocol are summarized in Table 18. The names and contact information for individuals who serve or have served in these roles is provided in Appendix E.

Qualifications

Each position identified in Table 18 requires minimum background knowledge, skills, and abilities. The project lead must be familiar with methods to provide climate data that are useful to national park managers. This includes familiarity with relevant datasets, data requirements, data processing, and quality assurance methods, analysis tools and approaches, and professional written and verbal communication of scientific results and ideas. The project lead will apply data preparation and computer analysis techniques that meet current standards of the climate science community. The NPS leads must be familiar with the objectives, standards, and requirements for the NPS I&M Program and each network and act as a liaison between the project lead and network park natural resource managers. The network data managers must work with the NPS and project leads to understand and provide input on data management activities.

Annual Workload and Schedule

The project lead will generally begin assembling annual status reports in January immediately after the calendar year of interest concludes. Due to a lag-time in the availability of quality controlled and checked data, as well as the availability of derived products (e.g., PRISM maps), it is expected that these draft reports will be completed roughly six months after the end of the calendar year (i.e., by June). These reports will be peer-reviewed by at least the NPS leads (see Roles and Responsibilities section below) and respective park natural resource managers. The NPS leads will periodically and with appropriate lead time amend the Cooperative Agreement

Table 18. Roles and responsibilities for weather and climate monitoring.

Role	Responsibilities	Position
NPS lead	<ul><li>Implements program and provides oversight, administration, and budget tracking</li><li>Serves as NPS key official, agreement technical representative, contracting officers technical representative on agreements or contracts</li><li>Reviews reports and other products for completeness and compliance with I&M Program guidance and specifications</li><li>Assists Data Manager with data certification.</li><li>Liaison to WASO programs, offices, and other I&M networks</li><li>Coordinates changes to the protocol</li></ul>	ERMN and MIDN Program Managers
Project lead	<ul><li>Plans and coordinates project operations, namely the acquisition, analysis and reporting of climate data</li><li>Prepares data summaries and analytical results</li><li>Interprets data and prepares reports and other products</li><li>Performs or oversees maintenance and archiving of project records and data</li><li>Maintains web mapping portal for data delivery</li><li>Delivers certified data to NPS Data Manager annually</li></ul>	Pennsylvania State Climatologist (PASC)
NPS Data Manager	<ul><li>Advises on data and information management activities</li><li>Posts data, metadata, reports, and other products to NPS data storage and delivery systems and network Web sites</li></ul>	ERMN and MIDN Data Managers

with PASC to ensure no gaps in project support. Periodic "variability and trends" reports will be developed on a mutually agreeable (between the NPS and Project leads) timeline but no less frequently than one report every five years.

Data Acquisition and Archiving
Procedures for downloading and archiving station data are described in the Data Management section. Procedures are automated but do require some training and specialized skills and technical expertise. PASC is responsible for data acquisition and data certification. Archiving of certified data will be the responsibility of the ERMN and MIDN data managers and will occur at least once per year.

Facility and Equipment Needs
This protocol requires no specialized equipment or facilities for ERMN and MIDN personnel.

Budget Considerations
All relevant climate stations and datasets utilized by this protocol are funded by external agencies. Each network's annual fixed-cost budget is expected to cover facilities, computer hardware and standard software for the NPS leads and data managers as well as their time required to implement this protocol. Therefore, the expenses incurred by the ERMN and MIDN are solely to the cooperator chosen to serve as the project lead. The current Cooperative Agreement with the Office of the Pennsylvania State Climatologist specifies that the annual weather and climate summary reports (including data acquisition, management, analysis, and presentation/access via the Web portal) will be completed for $12,500 per year (split equally between the ERMN and MIDN). In addition, the Cooperative Agreement specifies that the Office of the Pennsylvania State Climatologist will also produce two long-term precipitation and temperature variability and trend reports during the next five years at a cost of $4,800 per report.

Initial protocol development, which included the station inventory (Appendix B), development of the Web portal, and prototype annual weather and climate reports cost roughly $40,000.

Revising the Protocol
The protocol will be reviewed and improved in conjunction with preparing periodic climate trend and inter-annual variability reports. This may be on a three- to five-year cycle depending on the network. The project and NPS leads and others will review the narrative, SOPs, associated database, and other products. Changes are logged according to procedures outlined in the following section.

The protocol narrative and each SOP contain a Revision History log that is completed for each change to explain reasons for changes and to assign a new version number to the revised SOP or narrative. Careful documentation of changes to the protocol and a library of previous protocol versions are essential for maintaining consistency in data acquisition and for appropriate treatment of the data during data summary and analysis.

Literature Cited

Bonan, G. B. 2002. Ecological Climatology: Concepts and Applications. Cambridge University Press.

Callahan, K. K., and S. M. Wakamiya. 2009. Mid-Atlantic Network data management plan. Natural Resource Report NPS/MIDN/NRR—2009/077. National Park Service, Fort Collins, CO.

Chapin III, F. S., M. S. Torn, and M. Tateno. 1996. Principles of ecosystem sustainability. The American Naturalist 148:1016–1037.

Comiskey, J. A., and K. K. Callahan, 2008. Mid-Atlantic Network vital signs monitoring plan. Natural Resource Report NPS/MIDN/NRR—2008/071. National Park Service. Fort Collins, CO.

Davey, C. A., K. T. Redmond, and D. B. Simeral. 2006a. Weather and climate inventory. National Park Service. National Park Service, Eastern Rivers and Mountains Network. Natural Resource Technical Report NPS/ERMN/NRTR—2006/006. National Park Service, Fort Collins, CO.

Davey, C. A., K. T. Redmond, and D. B. Simeral. 2006b. Weather and climate inventory, National Park Service, Mid-Atlantic Network. Natural Resource Technical Report NPS/MIDN/NRTR—2006/013. National Park Service, Fort Collins, CO.

Doesken, N. J., and A. Judson. 1997. The Snow Booklet: A Guide to the Science, Climatology, and Measurement of Snow in the United States. Colorado Climate Center, Department of Atmospheric Science, Colorado State University, Fort Collins, CO. pp. 86.

Durre, I., M. J. Menne, B. E. Gleason, T. G. Houston, and R. S. Vose. 2010. Comprehensive Automated Quality Assurance of Daily Surface Observations. Journal of Applied Meteorology and Climatology 49:1615-1633.

Fancy, S. G., J. E. Gross, and S. L. Carter. 2009. Monitoring the condition of natural resources in US national parks. Environmental Monitoring and Assessment 151:161–174.

Frumhoff, P. C., J. J. McCarthy, J. M. Melillo, S. C. Moser, and D. J. Wuebbles. 2007. Confronting climate change in the U.S. Northeast: science, impacts, and solutions. Synthesis report of the Northeast Climate Impacts Assessment (NECIA). Union of Concerned Scientists (UCS), Cambridge, MA.

Gray, S. T. 2008. Framework for linking climate, resource inventories, and ecosystem monitoring. Natural Resource Technical Report NPS/GRYN/NRTR—2008/110. National Park Service, Fort Collins, CO.

Jacobson, M. C., R. J. Charlson, H. Rodhe, and G. H. Orians. 2000. Earth System Science: From Biogeochemical Cycles to Global Change. Academic Press, San Diego, CA.

Kittel, T. 2008. The Development and Analysis of Climate Datasets for National Park Science and Management: A Guide to Methods for Making Climate Records Useful and Tools to Explore Critical Questions. Report prepared for the National Park Service Inventory and Monitoring Program. University of Colorado, Institute of Arctic and Alpine Research, Boulder, CO.

Kittel, T., S. Ostermann-Kelm, B. Frakes, M. Tercek, S. Gray, and C. Daly. 2009. A framework for climate analysis and reporting for Greater Yellowstone (GRYN) and Rocky Mountain (ROMN) networks: A report from the GRYN/ROMN climate data analysis workshop, Bozeman, Montana, 7–8 April 2009. Final draft. Prepared for the National Park Service, Greater Yellowstone Inventory and Monitoring Program, Bozeman, Montana, USA.

Knight, P., T. Wisniewski, C. Bahrmann, and S. Miller. 2010. Fort Necessity National Battlefield and Friendship Hill National Historic Site: Weather of 2009. Natural Resource Data Series NPS/ERMN/NRDS—2010/084. National Park Service, Fort Collins, Colorado.

Lin, X., K. G. Hubbard, E. A. Walter-Shea, J. R. Brandle, and G. E. Meyer. 2001. Some perspectives on recent *in situ* air temperature observations: Modeling the microclimate inside the radiation shields. J. Atmos. Oceanic Technol. 18:1470–1484.

Menne, M. J., C. N. Williams, Jr., and R. S. Vose. 2009. The United States historical climatology network monthly temperature data version 2. Bull. Amer. Meteor. Soc. 90:993–1007.

Marshall, M. R., and N. B. Piekielek. 2007. Eastern Rivers and Mountains Network Ecological Monitoring Plan. Natural Resource Report NPS/ERMN/NRR—2007/017. National Park Service. Fort Collins, CO.

Oakley, K. L., L. P. Thomas, and S. G. Fancy. 2003. Guidelines for long-term monitoring protocols. Wildlife Society Bulletin 31:1000–1003.

Piekielek, N. B. 2006 (Revised December 2009). Eastern Rivers and Mountains Network Data Management Plan. Natural Resource Report NPS/NER/NRR—2009/020. National Park Service. Philadelphia, PA.

Schlesinger, W. H. 1997. Biogeochemistry: An Analysis of Global Change. Academic Press, San Diego.

Appendix A. Data sources.

Introduction

The approach of the Eastern Rivers and Mountains and Mid-Atlantic networks Weather and Climate Monitoring Protocol is to acquire data from existing weather and climate observing programs that provide consistent, long-term, and high-quality records for our regions and then provide the critical steps of summarizing, reporting, and interpreting status and trends in several key climate elements. Here, we describe the purpose each of these weather and climate observing networks/programs including the Cooperative Observer Network, Remote Automated Weather Stations, Automated Surface Observing System, Clean Air Status and Trends Network, Road Weather Information System, several drought indices, and the Parameter-elevation Regressions on Independent Slopes Model as well as the North American Regional Reanalysis dataset. While some of these programs provide direct weather observations and data, others use observational data to produce models that provide sophisticated spatial interpolation across the entire domain.

National Weather Service - Cooperative Observer Program

http://www.nws.noaa.gov/om/coop/

The National Weather Service (NWS) daily Cooperative Observer Network (COOP) Stations have been a foundation of the U.S. climate program for decades and has long served as the main climate observation network in the United States. The NWS-COOP was formally created in 1890 under the Organic Act (although many individual weather stations were already in existance) with a mission to: (1) provide observational meteorological data required to define U.S. climate and help measure long-term climate changes; and (2) provide observational meteorological data in near real-time to support forecasting and warning mechanisms and other public service programs of the NWS. COOP stations are established, supervised, inspected, and maintained by NWS personnel.

Although some COOP stations have electronic instrumentation, they lack automated transmission capability. Daily observations are obtained by personnel directly reading the instruments (e.g., min-max thermometers and rain gauges) or by reading digital displays connected to electronic sensors. Core observations include: daily maximum and minimum temperature, daily observation-time temperature, and daily liquid precipitation (rain and water equivalent of snow) at some stations. Additional measurements may include snowfall and snow depth, pan evaporation, river stage, and special phenomena, such as hail and damaging winds. Data from COOP stations are transmitted to designated regional offices of the NWS or directly to the National Climatic Data Center (NCDC) in Asheville, NC immediately after the 24-hour temperature and precipitation observations are recorded. Observers then send data forms monthly to NCDC where data are digitized, checked, and archived.

At the time of writing, several major changes are underway within the Cooperative Observer Program. First, about 60 percent of all US COOP stations are now being entered with Weather Coder III or with IV-ROCS (which then is routed through Weather Coder), or about 3,500 stations. Soon, this will include most or all of the ERMN/MIDN COOP stations. This features immediate electronic entry and QC via the Web. In fact, the paper form is going extinct, and soon only digital records will be available at about 80 percent of the stations in the USA. Second, is the switch at NCDC from TD3200 format to GHCN (Daily Global Historical Climate

Network) and a whole range of associated changes, particularly as it related to data quality control. The COOP data quality control is now much more extensive in real-time as the electronically submitted data passes through several levels of quality assurance and is in a final format within a few days of submission.

More information on COOP data quality assurance and performance monitoring is provided at the following urls:

http://www.ncdc.noaa.gov/oa/hofn/coop/coop-home.html
http://ams.confex.com/ams/pdfpapers/131217.pdf
http://journals.ametsox.org/doi/pdf/10.1175/2010JAMC237531

United States Historical Climate Network
http://cdiac.ornl.gov/epubs/ndp/ushcn/ushcn.html

The United States Historical Climatology Network (USHCN) is a high-quality data set of daily and monthly records of basic meteorological variables from 1,218 observing stations across the 48 contiguous United States. Daily data include observations of maximum and minimum temperature, precipitation amount, snowfall amount, and snow depth; monthly data consist of monthly averaged maximum, minimum, and mean temperature and total monthly precipitation. Most of these stations are U.S. Cooperative Observing Network (COOP) stations located, generally, in rural locations, while some are National Weather Service First-Order stations that are often located in more urbanized environments. The USHCN has been developed over the years at the National Oceanic and Atmospheric Administration's (NOAA) National Climatic Data Center (NCDC) to assist in the detection of regional climate change. Furthermore, it has been widely used in analyzing U.S. climate. The period of record varies for each station. USHCN stations were chosen using a number of criteria, including length of record, percent of missing data, number of station moves and other station changes that may affect data homogeneity, and resulting network spatial coverage.

Remote Automated Weather Stations
http://raws.fam.nwcg.gov/
http://www.raws.dri.edu/

The multi-agency supported Remote Automated Weather Station (RAWS) network supports nearly 2,200 stations strategically located throughout the United States. These stations monitor the weather and provide weather data that assists land management agencies with a variety of projects such as monitoring air quality, rating fire danger, and providing information for research applications. RAWS data are used by fire-management personnel in various federal and state agencies to estimate a fire-danger rating in support of preventive measures, and to forecast the behavior of wildland fires. RAWS stations consist of automated sensors that record air temperature and relative humidity, precipitation, wind speed and direction, and measures of fuel moisture and temperature. Data are recorded every 15 minutes and are automatically transmitted to the National Interagency Fire Center (NIFC) in Boise, Idaho via the Geostationary Operational Environmental Satellite (GOES). The GOES is operated by the National Oceanic and Atmospheric Administration (NOAA). These data are automatically forwarded to several other computer systems, including the Weather Information Management System (WIMS) and the Western Regional Climate Center (WRCC) in Reno, Nevada.

Automated Surface Observation System

http://www.nws.noaa.gov/asos/

The Automated Surface Observing System (ASOS) network is a joint effort of the National Weather Service (NWS), the Federal Aviation Administration (FAA), and the Department of Defense (DOD). More than 900 ASOS stations are installed at (typically) major airports and military bases and are designed primarily to support aviation needs and weather forecast activities. These stations also support the needs of meteorological, hydrological, and climatological research communities. These stations collect easily accessible, high-quality data that can be coupled to historic climatic data from often co-located COOP sites (with long-term station records). ASOS stations are fully automated and collect hourly or sub-hourly observations. Meteorology elements that are measured include temperature, precipitation, humidity, wind, barometric pressure, dew point, sky cover, ceiling, visibility, and current weather. ASOS functions include measurement of weather elements, data processing and display, communication, and data storage (archiving). The ASOS automatically collects, processes, and error checks data and formats, displays, archives, and reports the weather elements included in a surface weather observation. Hourly data are archived by the NCDC.

Clean Air Status and Trends Network

http://www.epa.gov/castnet/

The Clean Air Status and Trends Network (CASTNet) is primarily an air-quality monitoring network managed by the Environmental Protection Agency (EPA). Established in 1987, CASTNet now comprises over 70 monitoring stations across the U.S. The majority of the monitoring stations are operated by the EPA and the data are also available through the EPA. Standard hourly weather and climate elements are measured and include temperature, wind, humidity, solar radiation, soil temperature, and sometimes moisture. These elements are intended to support interpretation of air-quality parameters that are also are measured at CASTNet sites. Data records at CASTNet sites are generally one to two decades in length.

US Geolgocal Survey Surface Water Data

http://waterdata.usgs.gov/nwis/sw

Nationally, USGS surfacewater data includes more than 850,000 station years of time-series data that describe stream levels, streamflow (discharge), reservoir and lake levels, surfacewater quality, and rainfall. The data are collected by automatic recorders and manual measurements at field installations across the Nation. Data are collected by field personnel or relayed through telephones or satellites to offices where it is stored and processed. The data relayed through the Geostationary Operational Environmental Satellite (GOES) system are processed automatically in near real time, and in many cases, real-time data are available online within minutes. Once a complete day of readings are received from a site, daily summary data are generated and stored in the data base. Recent provisional daily data are updated on the Web once a day when the computation is completed. Annually, the USGS finalizes and publishes the daily data in a series of water-data reports. Daily streamflow data and peak data are updated annually following publication of the reports.

Road Weather Information System
http://www.aurora-program.org/what_is_rwis.cfm

At least 42 state departments of transportation (DOTs) and other public and private-sector agencies use road weather information systems (RWISs) to support highway-operations and maintenance decision making, public information messages, and weather forecasts by the meteorological community. RWIS can be defined as a combination of technologies that uses historic and current climatological data to develop road and weather information (for example, nowcasts and forecasts) to aid in roadway-related decision making. The three main elements of RWIS are environmental sensor system (ESS) technology to collect data; models and other advanced processing systems to develop forecasts and tailor the information into an easily understood format; and dissemination platforms on which to display the tailored information. Environmental Sensing Stations (ESS) are components of RWIS that provide environmental data. Many types of data can be collected, the most common type being weather (air temperature, amount and type of precipitation, visibility, dew point, relative humidity, and wind speed and direction) and road surface (pavement temperature, subsurface temperature, surface condition (dry, wet, frozen), amount of deicing chemical on the roadway, and freezing point of the road surface). Most data are recorded hourly.

Parameter-elevation Regressions on Independent Slopes Model
http://www.prism.oregonstate.edu/

Parameter-elevation Regressions on Independent Slopes Model (PRISM) is a climate mapping system that uses point measurements of precipitation, temperature, and other climatic factors to produce continuous, digital grid estimates of monthly, yearly, and event-based climatic parameters. Data extends back to 1895. It is offered at numerous spatial scales with the 800-meter grid being both free and of reasonably high resolution. The greatest utility of PRISM is that it presents the spatial distribution of temperature and precipitation, which single point observations are unable to provide. The model was originally developed to provide climate information at scales matching available land-cover maps to assist in ecological modeling and to address the extreme spatial and elevation gradients exhibited by the climate of the western United States. The PRISM technique accounts for the scale-dependent effects of topography on mean values of climate elements. Elevation provides the first-order constraint for the mapped climate fields, with slope and orientation (aspect) providing second-order constraints. The model has been enhanced gradually to address inversions, coast/land gradients, and climate patterns in small-scale trapping basins.

Monthly climate fields are generated by PRISM to account for seasonal variations in elevation gradients in climate elements. These monthly climate fields then can be combined into seasonal and annual climate records. Since PRISM maps are grid maps, they do not replicate point values but rather, for a given grid cell, represent the grid-cell average of the climate variable in question at the average elevation for that cell. The model relies on observed surface and upper-air measurements to estimate spatial climate fields. Data include: precipitation, maximum temperatures, minimum temperatures, dew point temperatures, and percent of normal precipitation.

North American Regional Reanalysis and Global Reanalysis
http://www.esrl.noaa.gov/psd/data/gridded/data.narr.html
http://wesley.wwb.noaa.gov/Reanalysis.html

NOAA's National Center for Atmospheric Prediction (NCEP) North American Regional Reanalysis (NARR) is a long-term, dynamically consistent, high-resolution, high-frequency, atmospheric and land surface hydrology dataset for the North American domain. It covers the 30+-year period of 1979–current. Essential components of the system used to generate NARR are the lateral boundaries from and the data used for the NCEP–DOE Global Reanalysis, the NCEP Eta Model and its Data Assimilation System, a recent version of the Noah land-surface model, and the use of numerous datasets additional to or improved compared to those of the global re-analyses. In particular, NARR has successfully assimilated high-quality and detailed precipitation observations into the atmospheric analysis. Consequently, the forcing to the land-surface model component of the system is more accurate than in previous re-analyses, so that NARR provides a much-improved analysis of land hydrology and land–atmosphere interaction. The overall atmospheric circulation throughout the troposphere has been substantially improved as well.

NCEP and National Center for Atmospheric Research (NCAR) have cooperated in a project (denoted "reanalysis" or "global reanalysis" or "GR") to produce a retroactive record of more than 60 years of global analyses of atmospheric fields in support of the needs of the research and climate monitoring communities. This effort involved the recovery of land surface, ship, rawinsonde, pibal, aircraft, satellite, and other data. These data were then quality controlled and assimilated with a data assimilation system kept unchanged over the reanalysis period. This eliminated perceived climate jumps associated with changes in the operational (real time) data assimilation system, although the reanalysis is still affected by changes in the observing systems. During the earliest decade (1948–57), there were fewer upper-air data observations and they were made 3 h later than the current main synoptic times (e.g.,0300 UTC), and primarily in the Northern Hemisphere, so that the reanalysis is less reliable than for the later 50 years. The reanalysis data assimilation system continues to be used with current data in real time (Climate Data Assimilation System or CDAS), so that its products are available from 1948 to the present. The products include, in addition to the gridded reanalysis fields, 8-day forecasts every 5 days, and the binary universal format representation (BUFR) archive of the atmospheric observations. The products can be obtained from NCAR, NCEP, and from the National Oceanic and Atmospheric Administration/Climate Diagnostics Center (NOAA/CDC).

Drought Indices
http://www.drought.gov

There are a number of drought indices used to estimate the severity of drought in an area using algorithms that incorporate recent temperatures, rainfall, and soil moisture. The main indices we will report on are the Palmer Drought Severity Index (PDSI) and the Drought Monitor (DM) – Drought Intensity Index.

Palmer Drought Severity Index

http://lwf.ncdc.noaa.gov/oa/climate/research/prelim/drought/palmer.html

The Palmer Drought Severity Index (PDSI) is a soil moisture algorithm calibrated for relatively homogeneous regions and was the first comprehensive drought index developed in the United States. In 1989, a modified method to compute the PDSI was begun operationally. This modified PDSI differs from the PDSI during transition periods between dry and wet spells. The PDSI is calculated based on precipitation and temperature data, as well as the local available water content of the soil. The values vary between extremely moist (>4.0) and extreme drought (<-4.0) (see below). Ideally, the Palmer Index is designed so that a -4.0 in South Carolina has the same meaning in terms of the moisture departure from a climatological normal as a -4.0 in Idaho.

The PDSI has typically been calculated on a monthly basis, and a long-term archive of the monthly values for every climate division in the United States exists with the NCDC from 1895 through the present. There are considerable limitations to using PDSI because values may lag emerging droughts by several months; it is less well suited for mountainous land or areas of frequent climatic extremes; snowfall, snow cover, and frozen ground are not included in the index. However, despite these drawbacks it is widely reported and used to monitor drought and trigger relief programs.

Palmer Drought Severity Index Scale:

4.0 and above	=	Extremely Moist
3.0 to 3.9	=	Very Moist
2.0 to 2.9	=	Moderately Moist
-1.9 to 1.9	=	Near Normal
-2.0 to -2.9	=	Moderate Drought
-3.0 to -3.9	=	Severe Drought
-4.0 and less	=	Extreme Drought

Drought Monitor

http://www.drought.unl.edu/dm/monitor.html
http://www.drought.unl.edu/dm/classify.htm

The Drought Monitor is a synthesis of multiple indices and impacts and represents a consensus of federal (U.S. Department of Agriculture [USDA] and NOAA) and academic scientists (National Drought Mitigation Center at University of Nebraska-Lincoln). The Drought Monitor produces a summary map of drought intensity for the nation and all states each week. Drought intensity is classified based on the PDSI, the Standardized Precipitation Index (SPI), soil moisture, streamflow, and other indicators of drought such as vegetation health, groundwater levels, and snow-water-equivalent. It is on a scale ranging from abnormally dry (D0) to exceptional drought (D4). While the monitor provides excellent summary information on broad-scale conditions, local conditions (such as at the park scale) may vary.

Drought Monitor – Drought Intensity Scale:

D0 = Abnormally Dry
D1 = Moderate Drought
D2 = Severe Drought
D3 = Extreme Drought
D4 = Exceptional Drought

Appendix B. Station inventory and station ranking methodology. This appendix and additional supporting information can be accessed online at the National Park Service's Eastern Rivers and Mountains Network (http://science.nature.nps.gov/im/units/ermn/) and Mid-Atlantic Network (http://science.nature.nps.gov/im/units/midn/) websites.

Appendix C. Park survey responses. This appendix and additional supporting information can be accessed online at the National Park Service's Eastern Rivers and Mountains Network (http://science.nature.nps.gov/im/units/ermn/) and Mid-Atlantic Network (http://science.nature.nps.gov/im/units/midn/) websites.

Appendix D. Weather and climate observing stations. This appendix and additional supporting information can be accessed online at the National Park Service's Eastern Rivers and Mountains Network (http://science.nature.nps.gov/im/units/ermn/) and Mid-Atlantic Network (http://science.nature.nps.gov/im/units/midn/) websites.

Appendix E. Protocol personnel. This appendix identifies past and current names and contact information of various personnel identified in the protocol narrative. Titles of positions/roles in Table E.1 are based on those in the Operational Requirements section of the protocol narrative. Current personnel are listed in Table E.1 and, when relevant, past personnel will be listed in a separate table.

Table E.1. Name and contact information for individuals associated with this protocol.

Role	Name and Position	Start Date	End Date	Address	Phone	E-mail
Project Lead	Paul Knight, Pennsylvania State Climatologist	January 1, 2011	Current	605A Walker Building University Park, PA 16802	814-863-1842	pgk2@psu.edu
NPS Lead	Matt Marshall, ERMN Program Manager	January 1, 2011	Current	420 Forest Resources Building University Park, PA 16802	814-863-0134	matt_marshall@nps.gov
NPS Lead	Jim Comiskey, MIDN Program Manager	January 1, 2011	Current	120 Chatham Lane Fredericksburg, VA 22405	540-654-5328	jim_comiskey@nps.gov
Data Manager	Kristina Callahan, ERMN Data Manager	January 1, 2011	Current	422 Forest Resources Building University Park, PA 16802	814-863-2320	kristina_callahan@nps.gov
Data Manager	Sara Wakamiya, MIDN Data Manager	January 1, 2011	Current	120 Chatham Lane Fredericksburg, VA 22405	540-654-5538	sarah_wakamiya@nps.gov

NPS 962/113170, March 2012

www.ingramcontent.com/pod-product-compliance
Lightning Source LLC
Chambersburg PA
CBHW081139290526
45795CB00006B/2298